THE COMPLETE KEYBOARD PLAYER

GREATEST HITS

Exclusive Distributors:
MUSIC SALES LIMITED
8/9 Frith Street, London W1V 5TZ, England.

MUSIC SALES PTY LIMITED
120 Rothschild Avenue, Rosebery, NSW 2018, Australia.

Order No. AM952677
ISBN 0-7119-7279-6
This book © Copyright 1998 by Wise Publications

Compiled by Peter Evans
Music arranged by Kenneth Baker
Cover design by Chloë Alexander
Photographs courtesy of London Features International
Printed in the United Kingdom by Redwood Books Ltd, Trowbridge, Wilts.

YOUR GUARANTEE OF QUALITY
As publishers, we strive to produce every book to the highest commercial standards.
This book has been carefully designed to minimise awkward page turns and to make playing from it a real pleasure.
Particular care has been given to specifying acid-free, neutral-sized paper made from pulps which have not been elemental chlorine bleached. This pulp is from farmed sustainable forests and was produced with special regard for the environment.
Throughout, the printing and binding have been planned to ensure a sturdy, attractive publication which should give years of enjoyment.
If your copy fails to meet our high standards, please inform us
and we will gladly replace it.

Music Sales' complete catalogue describes thousands of titles and is available in full colour sections by subject, direct from Music Sales Limited. Please state your areas of interest and send a cheque/postal order for £1.50 for postage to: Music Sales Limited, Newmarket Road, Bury St. Edmunds, Suffolk IP33 3YB.

Visit the Internet Music Shop at
http://www.musicsales.co.uk

THIS PUBLICATION IS NOT AUTHORISED FOR SALE IN THE
UNITED STATES OF AMERICA AND/OR CANADA.

WISE PUBLICATIONS
LONDON/NEW YORK/PARIS/SYDNEY/COPENHAGEN/MADRID

A Whiter Shade Of Pale

Words & Music by Keith Reid & Gary Brooker

Voice: pipe organ + chorus
Rhythm: rock
Tempo: slow (♩ = 72)

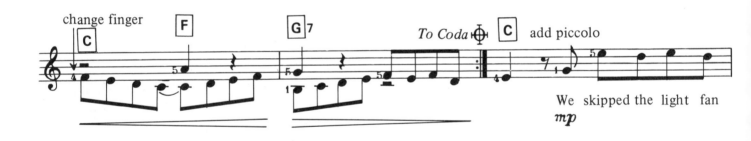

We skipped the light fan

dan- go, ____ and turned cart-wheels 'cross the floor. _____

I was feel-ing kind of sea- sick, __ but the crowd called out for

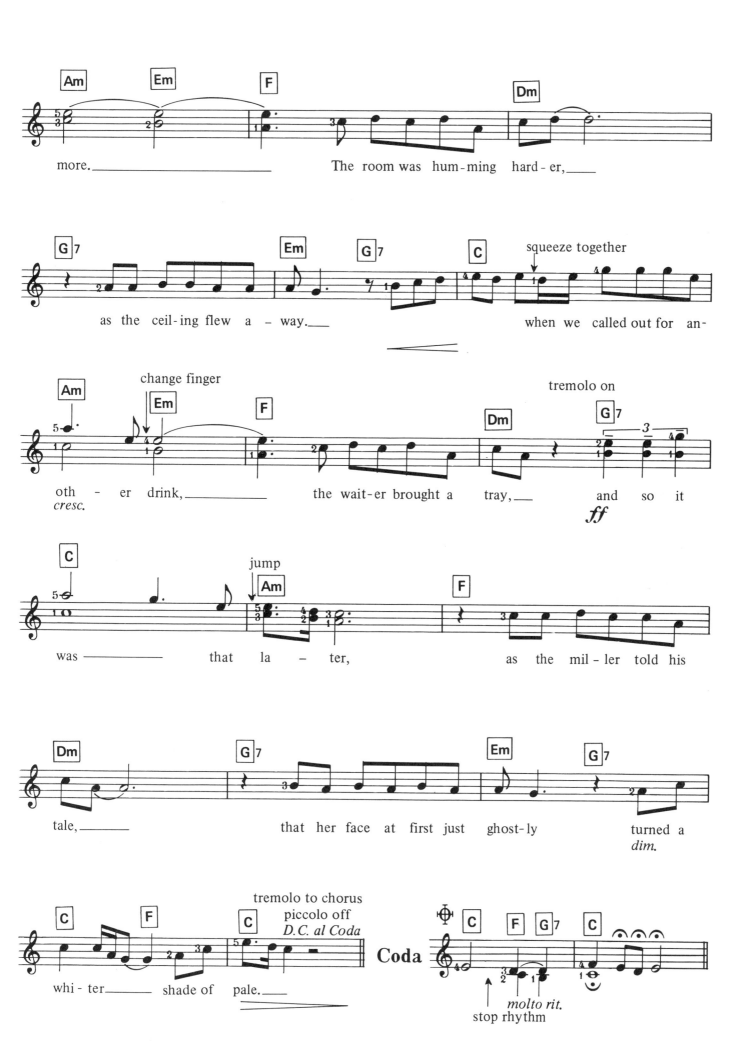

more._____ The room was hum-ming hard-er,_____ as the ceil-ing flew a – way.___ when we called out for an-

oth – er drink,_____ the wait-er brought a tray,__ and so it was _____ that la – ter, as the mil – ler told his

tale,_____ that her face at first just ghost-ly turned a whi-ter____ shade of pale.___

A WHOLE NEW WORLD (FROM WALT DISNEY PICTURES' "ALADDIN")

MUSIC BY ALAN MENKEN | LYRICS BY TIM RICE

Voice: vibraphone
Rhythm: 8 beat
Tempo: medium (♩ = 96)

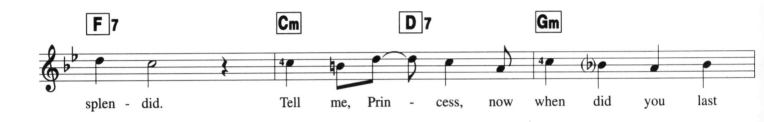

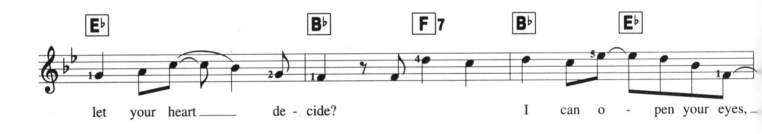

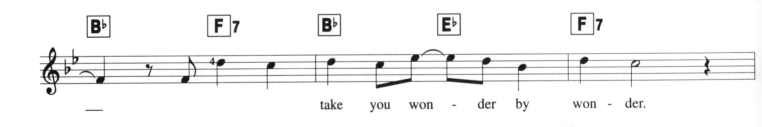

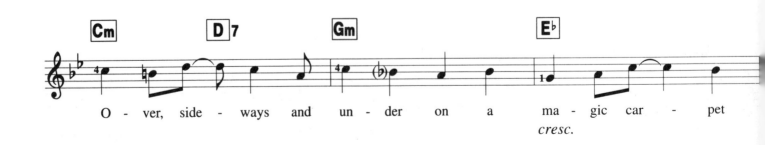

A Woman In Love

Words & Music by Barry Gibb & Robin Gibb

Voice: flute
Rhythm: rock
Tempo: medium (♩ = 96)

VERSES

1. Life is a mo-ment in space,__ when the dream is gone,__ it's a lone-li-er place.
2. With you e-ter-nal-ly mine,_____ in love there is _____ no ____ mea-sure of time.
   mp

I kiss the morn-ing good - bye, ____ but down in - side__
We planned it all at the start, ____ that you and I____
cresc.

____ you know we ne - ver know why.____ The road is nar-row and long,__
____ live in each oth-er's heart.____ We may be o-ceans a - way,__
                                              mf   *mp*

____ when eyes meet eyes, ____ and the feel - ing is strong. ____
____ you feel my love, ____ I hear what you say. _____

I turn a - way from the wall, _____ I stum-ble and fall, _____ but I give you it all.__
The truth is ev - er a lie, _____ I stum-ble and fall, _____ but I give you it all.__
cresc.

8

CHORUS

All My Loving

WORDS & MUSIC BY JOHN LENNON & PAUL MCCARTNEY

Voice: jazz organ + rock guitar + chorus (chorale). Duet on (if available)
Rhythm: shuffle (or swing)
Tempo: medium (♩ = 126)
Synchro-start

Close your eyes and I'll kiss you, to -

mor - row I'll miss you, re - mem - ber I'll

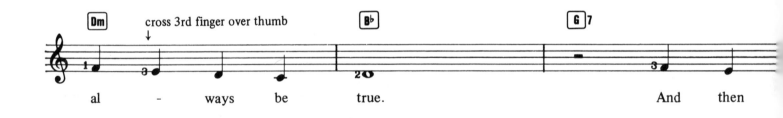

al - ways be true. And then

while I'm a - way, I'll write home ev - 'ry

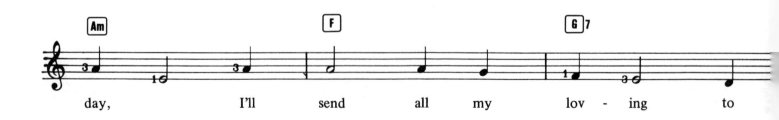

day, I'll send all my lov - ing to

C

tremolo on new hand position Am

you. All my lov · ing

new hand position

I will send to you. All my

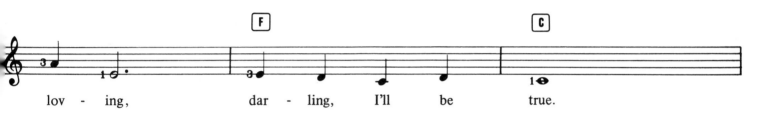

F C

lov - ing, dar - ling, I'll be true.

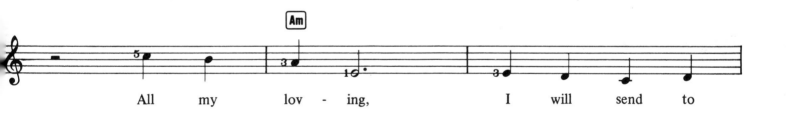

Am

All my lov - ing, I will send to

you. All my lov - ing,

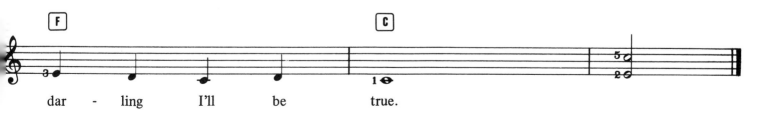

F C

dar - ling I'll be true.

AMERICA

Music by Leonard Bernstein | Lyrics by Stephen Sondheim

Voice: brass ensemble + piccolo
Rhythm: samba (♩ = ♩ Spread rhythm over two bars)
Tempo: medium (♩. = 108)

CHORUS

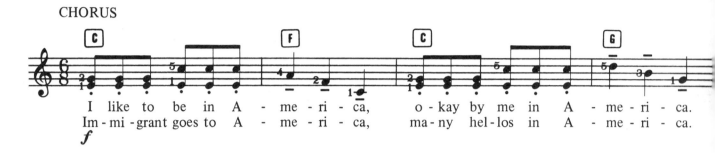

I like to be in A - me - ri - ca, o - kay by me in A - me - ri - ca.
Im - mi - grant goes to A - me - ri - ca, ma - ny hel - los in A - me - ri - ca.

f

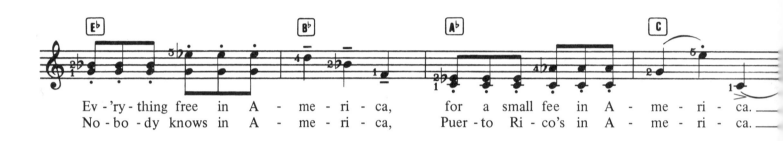

Ev - 'ry - thing free in A - me - ri - ca, for a small fee in A - me - ri - ca.
No - bo - dy knows in A - me - ri - ca, Puer - to Ri - co's in A - me - ri - ca.

cut piccolo

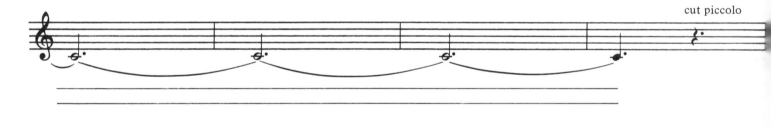

VERSE

I like the ci - ty of San Juan.___ I know a boat you can get on.___
When I will go back to San Juan.___ When you will shut up and get gone?___

mp

___ Hun - dreds of flow - ers in full bloom.___ Hun - dreds of peo - ple in
___ I'll give them new wash - ing ma - chine.___ What have they got there to

each room!___
keep clean?___

CHORUS

Au-to-mo-bile in A - me - ri - ca,
I like the shores of A - me - ri - ca,

chro-mi-um steel in A - me - ri - ca.
com-fort is yours in A - me - ri - ca.

Wi - re spoke wheel in A - me - ri - ca,
Knobs on the doors in A - me - ri - ca,

ve - ry big deal in A - me - ri - ca.___
wall to wall floors in A - me - ri - ca.___

cut piccolo **VERSE**

I'll drive a Bu - ick through San Juan.___
I'll bring a T. V. to San Juan.___

If there's a road you can drive on.___
If there's a cur-rent to turn on.___

I'll give my cou-sins a
Ev - 'ry-one there will give

add piccolo *D.C. and Fade last time*

free ride. ___
big cheer. ___

How you fit all of them in - side?___
Ev - 'ry-one there will have moved here!___

ANOTHER DAY IN PARADISE
WORDS & MUSIC BY PHIL COLLINS

Voice: flute
Rhythm: rock
Tempo: medium (♩ = 104)

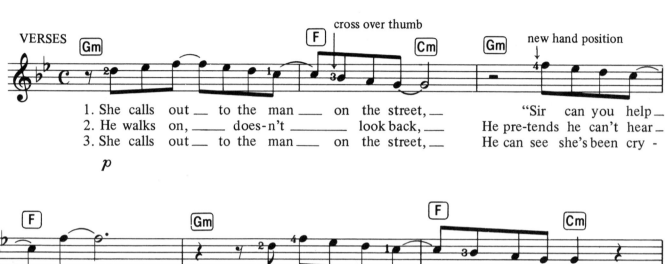

1. She calls out to the man on the street, "Sir can you help
2. He walks on, doesn't look back, He pre-tends he can't hear
3. She calls out to the man on the street, He can see she's been cry -

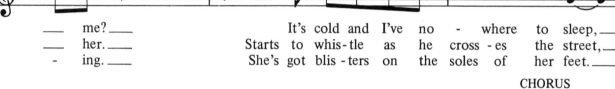

— me? It's cold and I've no - where to sleep,
— her. Starts to whis-tle as he cross - es the street,
- ing. She's got blis - ters on the soles of her feet.

CHORUS
flute to brass

is there some - where you can tell me?"
Seems em - bar - rassed to be there. Oh, think
She can't walk but she's try - ing.

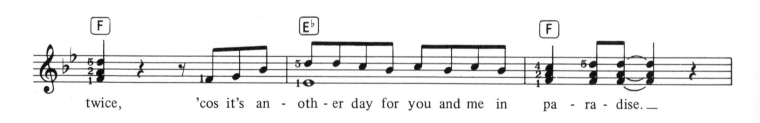

twice, 'cos it's an - oth - er day for you and me in pa - ra - dise.

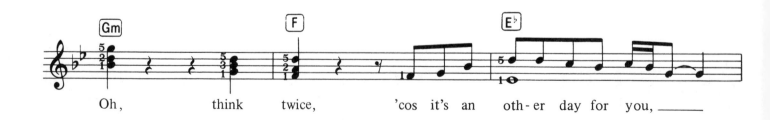

Oh, think twice, 'cos it's an oth - er day for you,

you and me in pa - ra - dise.

Just think a -

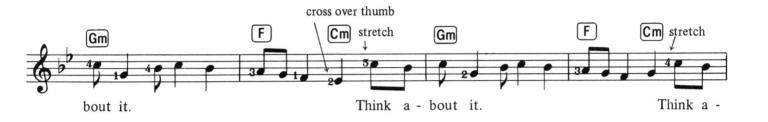

bout it.

Think a - bout it.

Think a -

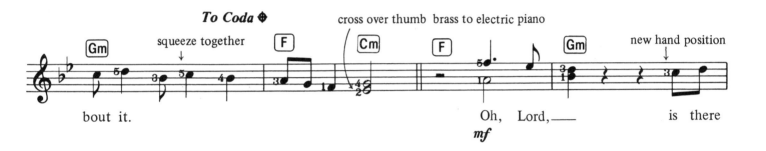

bout it.

Oh, Lord,____

is there

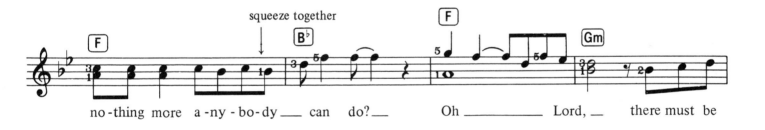

no-thing more a-ny-bo-dy____ can do?____ Oh ____ Lord, __ there must be

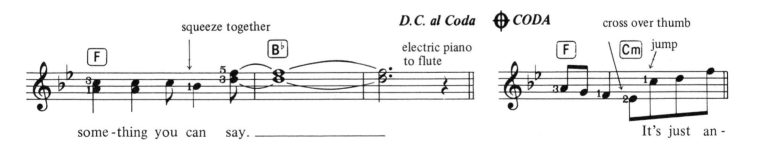

some-thing you can say. ____

It's just an -

oth - er day ____ for you and me ____ in pa - ra - dise. ____

It's just an -

15

BALLADE POUR ADELINE
COMPOSED BY PAUL DE SENNEVILLE

Voice: piano, with full sustain. Arpeggio, if available
Rhythm: beguine (or bossa nova)
Tempo: medium ($\quarter = 120$)

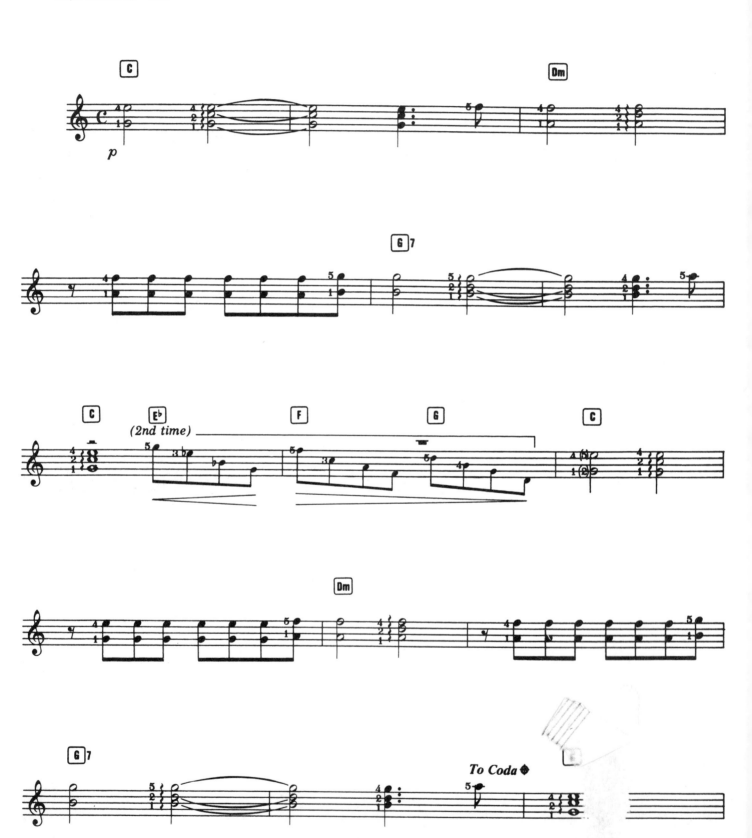

BLACK VELVET

WORDS & MUSIC BY CHRISTOPHER WARD & DAVID TYSON

Voice: guitar
Rhythm: swing
Tempo: medium (♩ = 100)

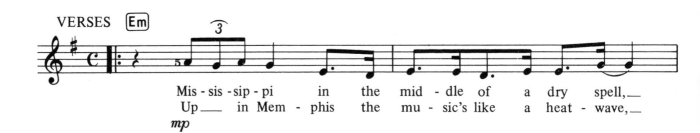

Mis - sis - sip - pi in the mid - dle of a dry spell,__
Up__ in Mem - phis the mu - sic's like a heat - wave,__

Jim - mie Rod - gers_ on the Vic - tr' - la up__ high.__
"White Light - ning"_____ bound to drive you_ wild. __
Ma - ma's danc - ing __ with
Ma - ma's ba - by's in the

ba - by__ on her shoul - der,__ the sun is set - ting like mo -
heart of __ ev - 'ry school girl,__ "Love Me Ten - der" leaves them

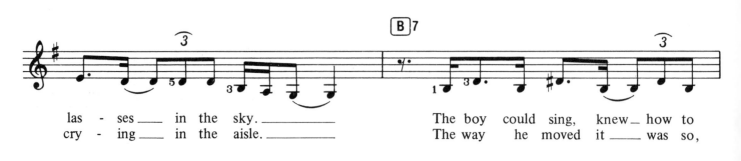

las - ses __ in the sky._____ The boy could sing, knew_ how to
cry - ing __ in the aisle._____ The way he moved it __ was so,

move __ ev - 'ry - thing,__ }
so _____ sweet and true,__ }
al - ways want - ing more,__ he'd leave you long - ing for:__
cresc.

CHORUS

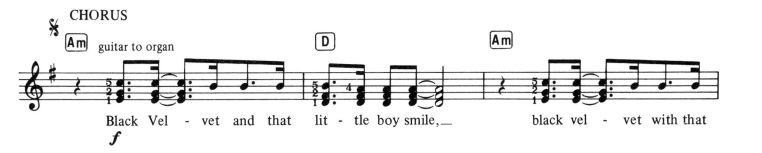

Black Vel - vet and that lit - tle boy smile,— black vel - vet with that

f

slow South-ern style. A new re-li - gion that-'ll bring ya— to your knees,

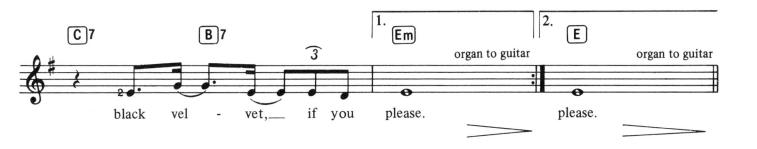

black vel - vet,— if you please. please.

organ to guitar   organ to guitar

INTERLUDE

Ev-'ry word— of ev-'ry song — that he sang— was for you.—

mp

In a flash— he was gone,— it hap-pened so

cresc.

D.S. (Repeat CHORUS and fade)

guitar to organ

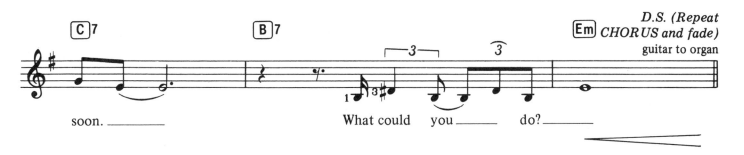

soon.— What could you— do?—

BYE BYE LOVE

WORDS & MUSIC BY FELICE & BOUDLEAUX BRYANT

Voice: jazz organ (with tremolo)
Rhythm: rock
Tempo: quite fast (♩ = 160)

VERSE

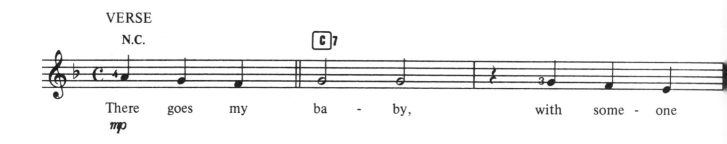

There goes my ba - by, with some - one

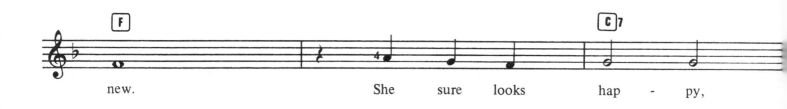

new. She sure looks hap - py,

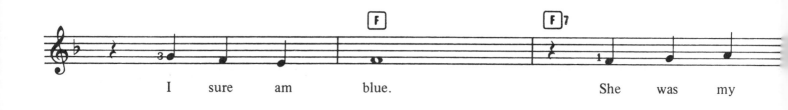

I sure am blue. She was my

ba - by, _____ till he stepped in.

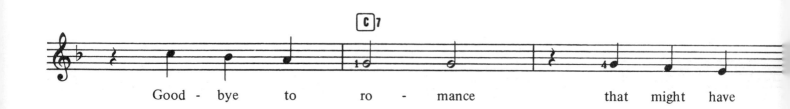

Good - bye to ro - mance that might have

CHORUS

been. _____ Bye, bye, love.

Bye, bye, hap - pi - ness. ____ Hel - lo

lone - li - ness, __ I think I'm gon - na cry.

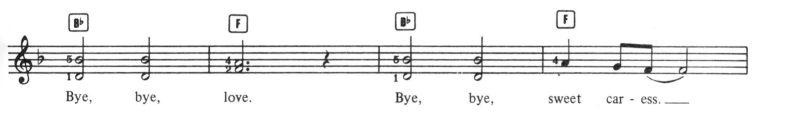

Bye, bye, love. Bye, bye, sweet car - ess. ____

Hel - lo emp - ti - ness, __ I feel like I could

die. Bye, bye, my love, bye, bye. stop rhythm

21

Barbara Ann

Words & Music by Fred Fassert

Voice: brass ensemble
Rhythm: rock
Tempo: fast (♩ = 160)

INTRO

(Bar - bar Ann, Bar - bar - bra Ann. Bar - bar Ann, Bar

ff

CHORUS

- bar - bra Ann)   Ann,   take my
Bar - bar

f

hand.   Bar - bar Ann,

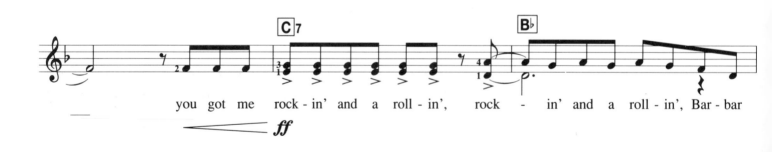

you got me rock - in' and a roll - in', rock - in' and a roll - in', Bar - bar

ff

brass to guitar   VERSES

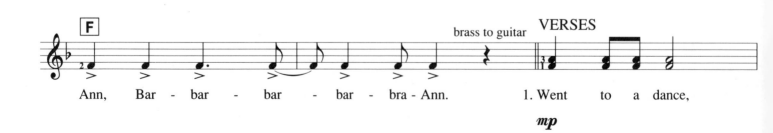

Ann, Bar - bar - bar - bar - bra - Ann.   1. Went to a dance,

mp

look - in' for ro - mance, saw Bar - bar Ann, so I thought I'd take a chance, oh Bar - bra

Ann, Bar - bra Ann, take my hand, oh, Bar - bra - Ann, Bar - bra - Ann,

mf

take my hand. You got me rock - in' and a roll - in', rock - in' and a roll - in', Bar - bra

f

Ann, Bar - bar bar - bar - bra Ann 2. Played my fav - 'rite tune,

mp

danced with Bet - ty Lou, tried Peg - gy Sue, but I knew they would - n't do, oh Bar - bra

Ann, Bar - bra Ann, take my hand, oh Bar - bra Ann, Bar - bra Ann,

mf

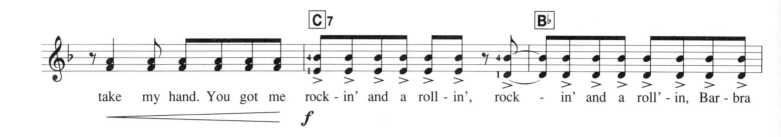

take my hand. You got me rock - in' and a roll - in', rock - in' and a roll' - in, Bar - bra

Ann, Bar - bar - bar - bar - bra Ann. (Bar - bar Ann, Bar

guitar to bass INTRO

- bar - bar Ann. Bar - bar Ann, Bar - bar - bra Ann.)

CHORUS

Bar - bar

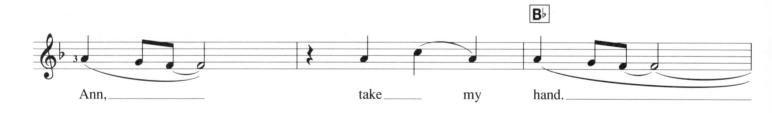

Ann, _____ take _____ my hand. _____

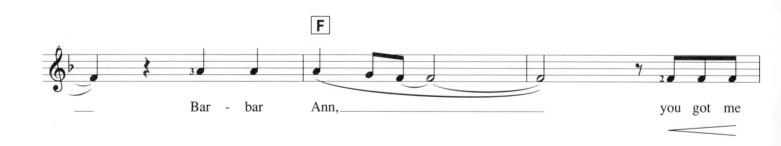

___ Bar - bar Ann, _____ you got me

rock - in' and a roll - in', rock - in' and a roll - in', Bar - bar Ann, Bar - bar - bar - bra Ann!

stop rhythm

Country House

Words & Music by Damon Albarn, Graham Coxon, Alex James & David Rowntree

Voice: trumpet
Rhythm: rock
Tempo: fast (♩ = 176)

INTRO

VERSES

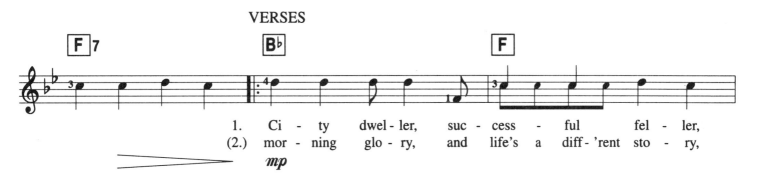

1. City dweller, successful feller,
(2.) morning glory, and life's a diff'rent story,

thought to himself, "Oops, I've got a lot of money, caught in a
ev'rythings going 'Jackanory,' in touch with his

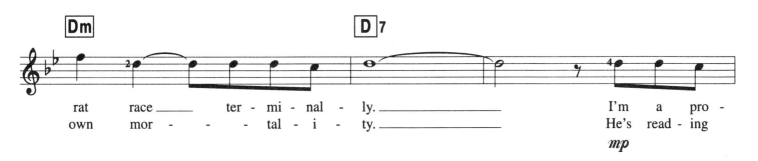

rat race terminally. I'm a pro-
own mortality. He's reading

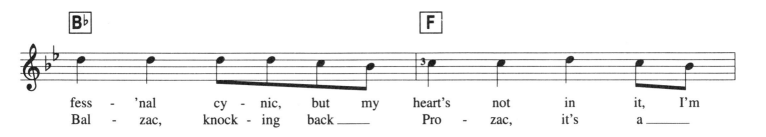

fess-'nal cynic, but my heart's not in it, I'm
Balzac, knocking back Prozac, it's a

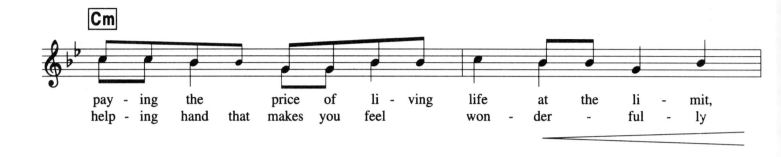

pay - ing the price of li - ving life at the li - mit,
help - ing hand that makes you feel won - der - ful - ly

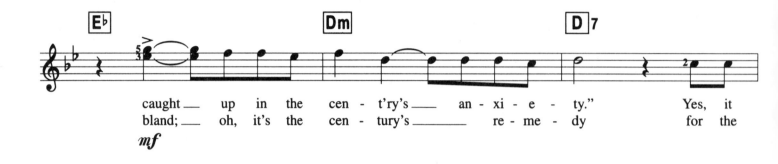

caught __ up in the cen - t'ry's __ an - xi - e - ty." Yes, it
bland; __ oh, it's the cen - tury's __ re - me - dy for the
mf

add guitar

preys on him, _____ he's get - ting thin. _____ Now he
faint at heart, _____ a new __ start. _____ *f*
cresc.

CHORUS

lives in a house, a ve - ry big house in the coun - 'try.

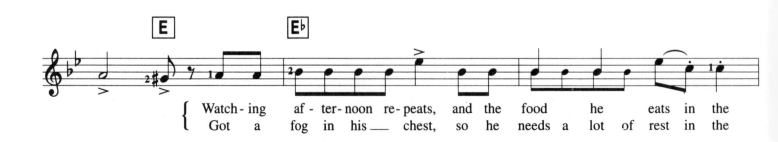

{ Watch - ing af - ter - noon re - peats, and the food he eats in the
Got a fog in his __ chest, so he needs a lot of rest in the

26

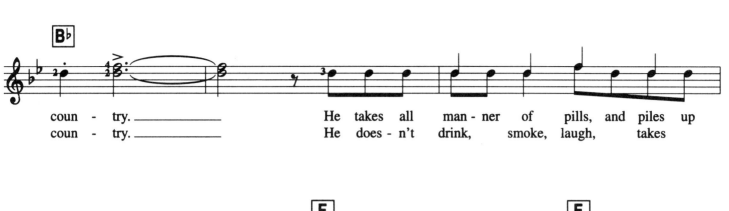

coun - try. _____ He takes all man - ner of pills, and piles up
coun - try. _____ He does - n't drink, smoke, laugh, takes

a - na - lyst's bills in the coun - try. Ooh, ___ it's like an
her - bal baths in the coun - try. Ooh, ___ but you'll

A - ni - mal Farm, lots of ru - ral charm in the coun - try.
come to no harm on the A - ni - mal Farm in the coun - try.

1.   **2.**   INTERLUDE

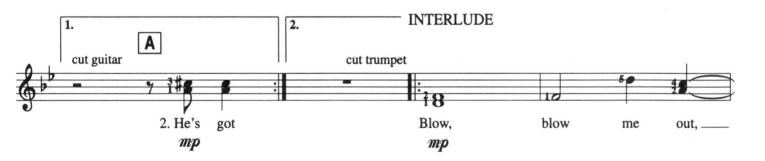

cut guitar   cut trumpet

2. He's got   Blow, blow me out, ___
mp   *mp*

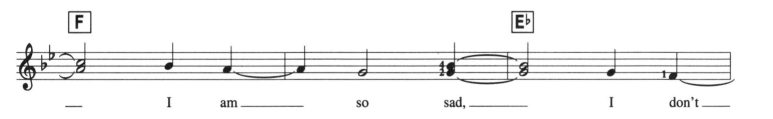

___ I am ___ so sad, ___ I don't ___

add trumpet

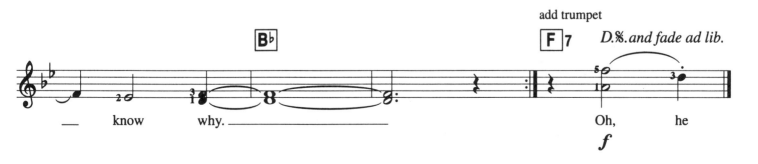

___ know why. _____ Oh, he
f

Can't Help Falling In Love

Words & Music by George Weiss, Hugo Peretti & Luigi Creatore

Voice: oboe
Rhythm: slow rock
Tempo: slow ($\quarternote = 96$)

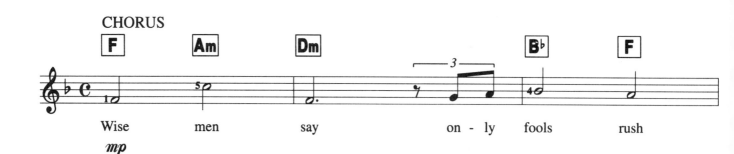

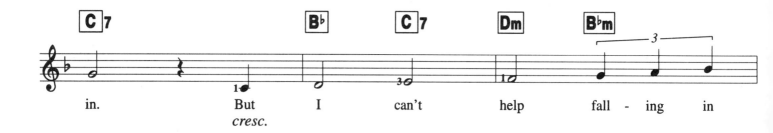

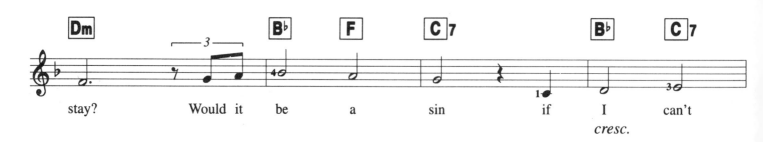

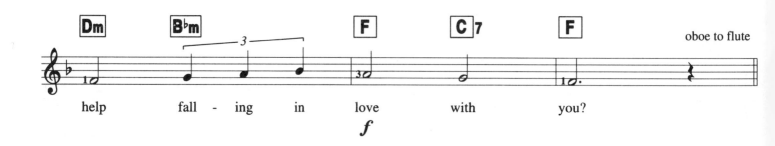

Come Fly With Me

Lyrics by Sammy Cahn | Music by James Van Heusen

Voice: trumpet
Rhythm: swing
Tempo: quite fast (♩ = 152)

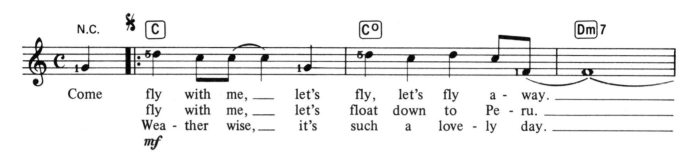

Come fly with me, ___ let's fly, let's fly a - way. ___
fly with me, ___ let's float down to Pe - ru. ___
Wea - ther wise, ___ it's such a love - ly day. ___

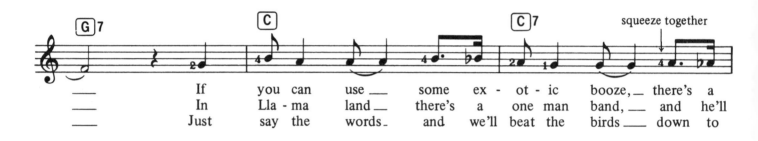

___ If you can use ___ some ex - ot - ic booze, ___ there's a
___ In Lla - ma land ___ there's a one man band, ___ and he'll
___ Just say the words ___ and we'll beat the birds ___ down to

bar in far Bom - bay, ___ come fly with me, let's
toot his flute for you, ___ come fly with me, let's
A - ca - pul - co Bay, ___ it's per - fect for a

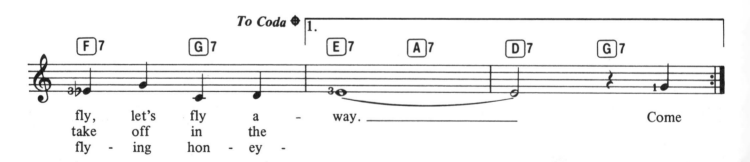

fly, let's fly a - way. ___ Come
take off in the
fly - ing hon - ey -

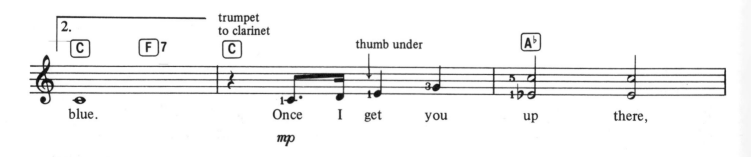

blue. Once I get you up there,

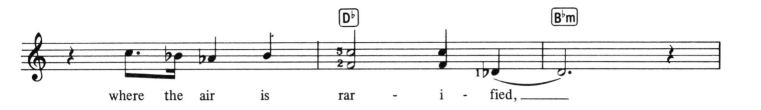

where the air is rar - i - fied, _____

we'll just glide, _____ star - ry eyed.

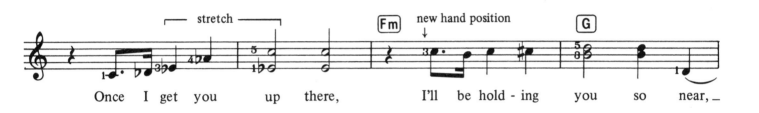

Once I get you up there, I'll be hold - ing you so near, __

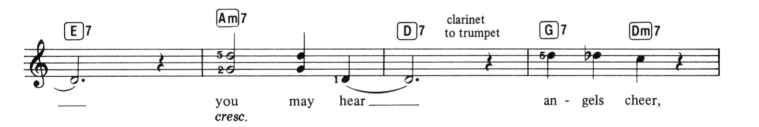

__ you may hear _____ an - gels cheer,

cresc.

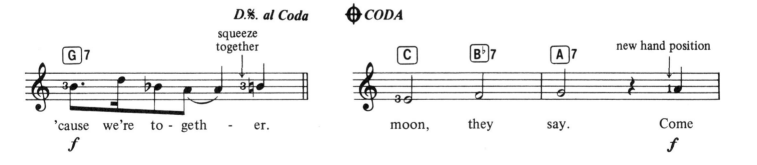

'cause we're to - geth - er.

f

moon, they say. Come

f

fly with me, __ let's fly, let's fly __ a - way.

ff

stop rhythm

DAY TRIPPER

WORDS & MUSIC BY JOHN LENNON & PAUL MCCARTNEY

Voice: guitar
Rhythm: rock
Tempo: medium (♩ = 69)
Synchro-start

(start rhythm)

Got a good rea - son _____ for
She's a big tea - ser, _____

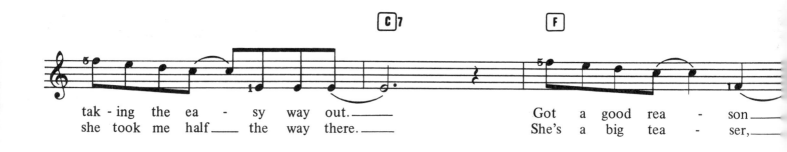

tak - ing the ea - sy way out. _____
she took me half ____ the way there. ____

Got a good rea - son
She's a big tea - ser,

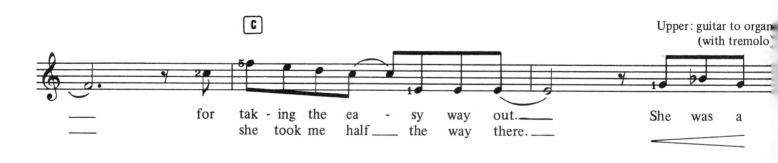

Upper: guitar to organ
(with tremolo)

____ for tak - ing the ea - sy way out. ____
____ she took me half ____ the way there. ____

She was a

day _____ trip - per, ____ one way tick - et,

yeh! It took me so _____ long ____ to find out,___

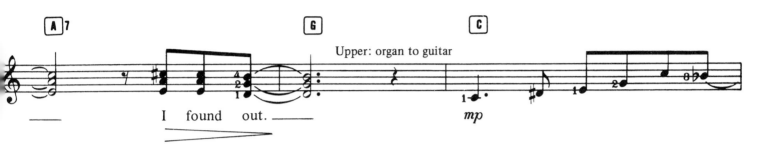

___ I found out. _____

Upper: organ to guitar

mp

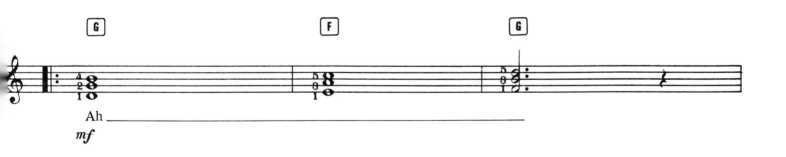

Ah _____

mf

(Repeat and Fade)

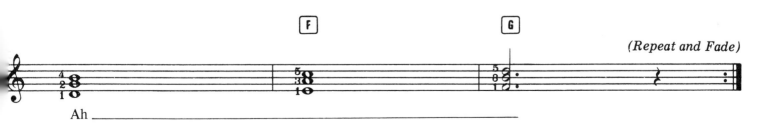

Ah _____

Do You Know The Way To San Jose

Words by Hal David | Music by Burt Bacharach

Voice: guitar
Rhythm: bossa nova
Tempo: fast (♩ = 176)

Do you know the way to San __ Jo-se? I've been a-way so
You can real-ly breathe in San __ Jo-se. They've got a lot of

mf

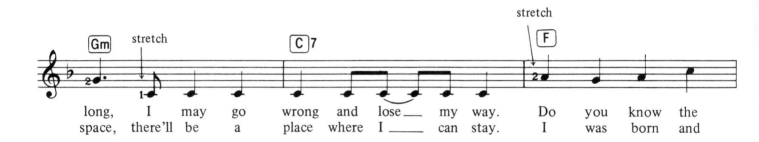

long, I may go wrong and lose __ my way. Do you know the
space, there'll be a place where I ___ can stay. I was born and

way to San __ Jo-se? I'm go-ing back to find some peace of
raised in San __ Jo-se. I'm go-ing back to find some peace of

guitar to vibes
new hand position

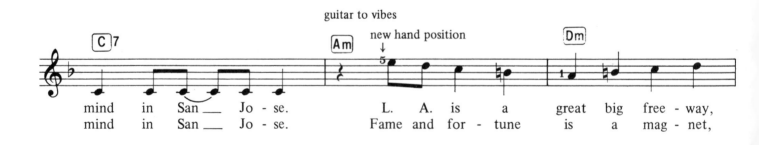

mind in San __ Jo-se. L. A. is a great big free-way,
mind in San __ Jo-se. Fame and for-tune is a mag-net,

Put a hun-dred down and buy a car.
it can pull you far a-way from home.

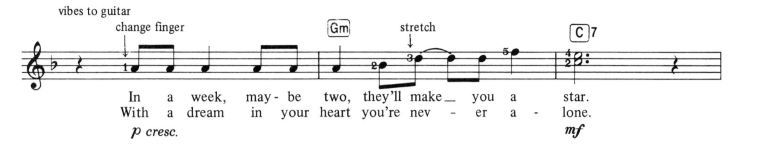

vibes to guitar
change finger | Gm | stretch | C 7

In a week, may-be two, they'll make ___ you a star.
With a dream in your heart you're nev - er a - lone.

p cresc. *mf*

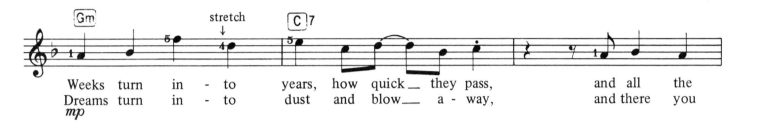

| Gm | stretch | C 7

Weeks turn in - to years, how quick ___ they pass, and all the
Dreams turn in - to dust and blow ___ a - way, and there you

mp

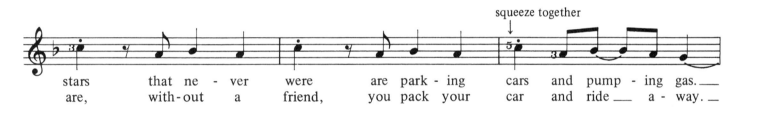

squeeze together

stars that ne - ver were are park - ing cars and pump - ing gas. ___
are, with - out a friend, you pack your car and ride ___ a - way. ___

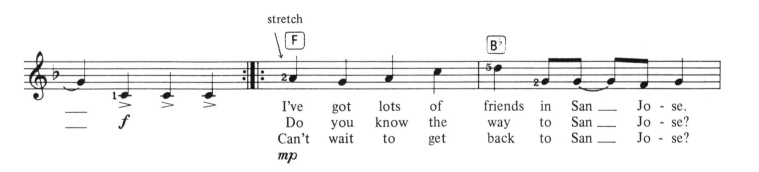

stretch
| F | | B♭ |

___ > > >
I've got lots of friends in San ___ Jo - se.
Do you know the way to San ___ Jo - se?
Can't wait to get back to San ___ Jo - se?

f   *mp*

new hand position
| F | cross over thumb   *(3 times)*

f   stop rhythm

Don't Know Much

Words by Cynthia Weil | Music by Barry Mann & Tom Snow

Voice: string ensemble
Rhythm: rock
Tempo: medium (♩ = 96)

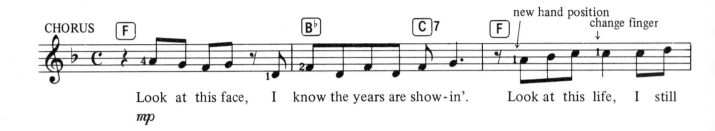

Look at this face, I know the years are show-in'. Look at this life, I still

don't know where it's go - in'. I don't know much, but I know I love you___

___ and that may be ___ all I need ___ to know. Look at these eyes, they've

ne - ver seen what mat-tered. Look at these dreams, so beat- en and so bat - tered.

I don't know much, but I know I love you, _____ and that may be ____

BRIDGE
strings to piano

all I need to know. So ma-ny ques-tions still left un ans-wered,
mp

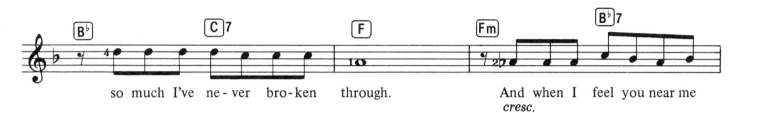

so much I've ne-ver bro-ken through. And when I feel you near me
cresc.

some-times I see so clear-ly the on-ly truth I've ev-er known is me and you.
f

CHORUS
piano to strings

squeeze together

Look at this man, so blessed with in-spi-ra-tion.
mp

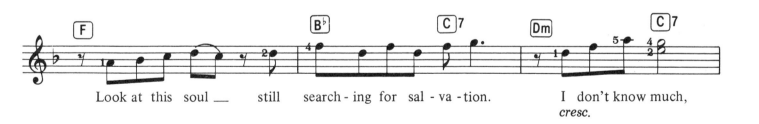

Look at this soul __ still search-ing for sal-va-tion. I don't know much,
cresc.

but I know I love you, ____ and that may be _____ all there is to know.
f

DOWNTOWN TRAIN

WORDS & MUSIC BY TOM WAITS

Voice: guitar
Rhythm: rock
Tempo: medium (♩ = 116)

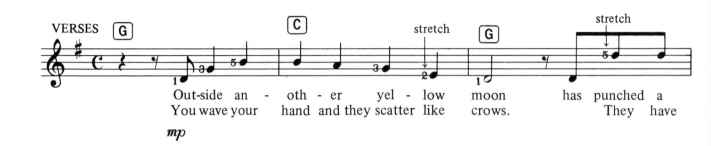

VERSES

Out-side an - oth - er yel - low moon has punched a
You wave your hand and they scatter like crows. They have

hole in the night - time, yes. I climb thru the win-dow, down to the
nothing that will capture your heart. They're just thorns — with - out the ___

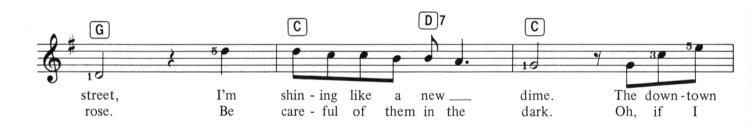

street, I'm shin - ing like a new ___ dime. The down-town
rose. Be care - ful of them in the dark. Oh, if I

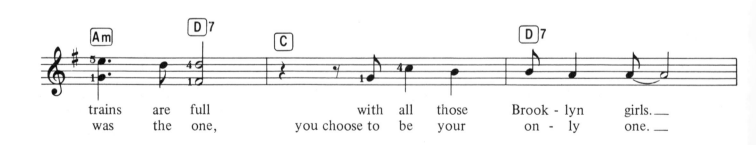

trains are full with all those Brook - lyn girls. ___
was the one, you choose to be your on - ly one. ___

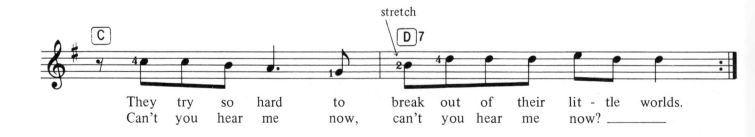

They try so hard to break out of their lit - tle worlds.
Can't you hear me now, can't you hear me now? _____

CHORUS
guitar to saxophone

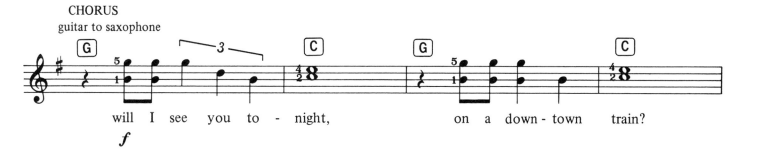

will I see you to - night, on a down - town train?

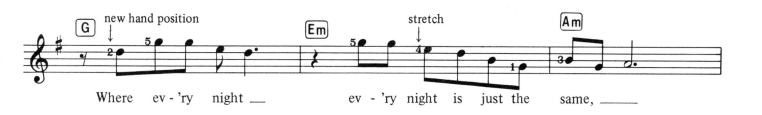

Where ev - 'ry night __ ev - 'ry night is just the same, _____

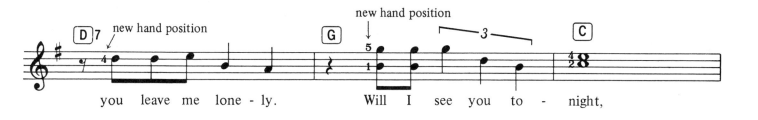

you leave me lone - ly. Will I see you to - night,

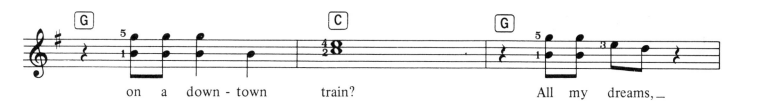

on a down - town train? All my dreams, _

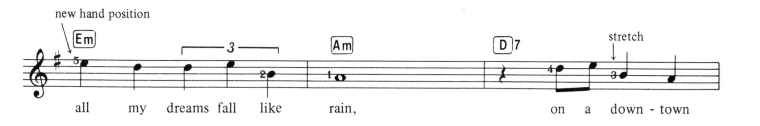

all my dreams fall like rain, on a down - town

train.

Eleanor Rigby

WORDS & MUSIC BY JOHN LENNON & PAUL McCARTNEY

Voice: string ensemble + arpeggio (if available)
Rhythm: rock
Tempo: medium (♩ = 120)

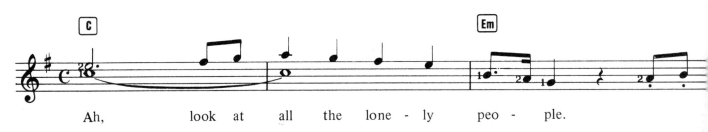

Ah, look at all the lone - ly peo - ple.

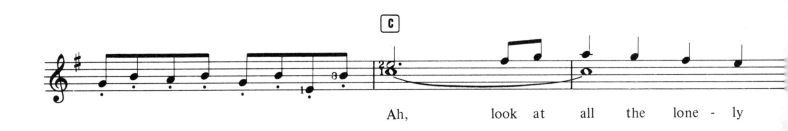

Ah, look at all the lone - ly

peo - ple. El - ea - nor Rig - by

picks up the rice___ in the church where a wed - ding has been.

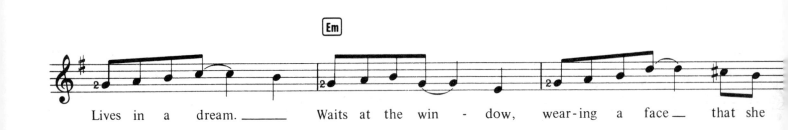

Lives in a dream.___ Waits at the win - dow, wear-ing a face___ that she

keeps in a jar by the door, who is it for?_____

All the lone - ly peo - ple, where do they all come from? All the lone - ly peo - ple, where do they all be - long? Ah, look at all the lone - ly peo - ple. Ah look at

D.S. al Fine

all the lone - ly peo - ple.

41

Feel Like Making Love

Words & Music by Eugene McDaniels

Voice: flute
Rhythm: rock
Tempo: medium ($\quarternote$ = 96)

Stroll-in' in the park, watch-in' win-ter turn to spring.

Walk-in' in the dark, see-in' lov-ers do their

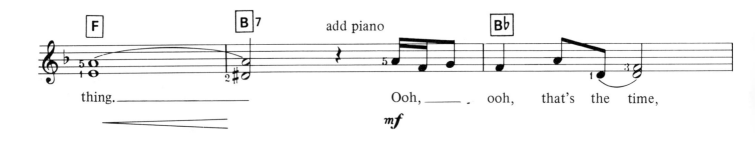

thing. Ooh, ___ ooh, that's the time,

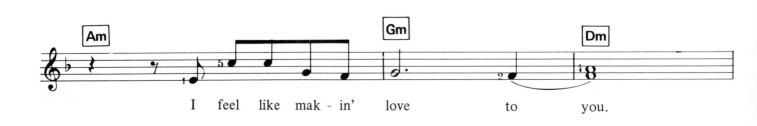

I feel like mak-in' love to you.

That's the time, I feel like mak-in' dreams come

true,_____ oh___ ba - by.___ When you talk to me

when you're moan-in' sweet and low._____

When you touch-a - me, and my feel-ings start to show._____

Ooh,_____ ooh, that's the time, I feel like mak-in'

love to you. That's the time I feel like mak-in'

dreams come true_____ oh___ ba - by.___

(Repeat & fade)

FEELINGS (DIME)

BY MORRIS ALBERT & LOUIS GASTE

Voice: bright piano (with tremolo)
Rhythm: bossa nova
Tempo: medium (♩ = 100)

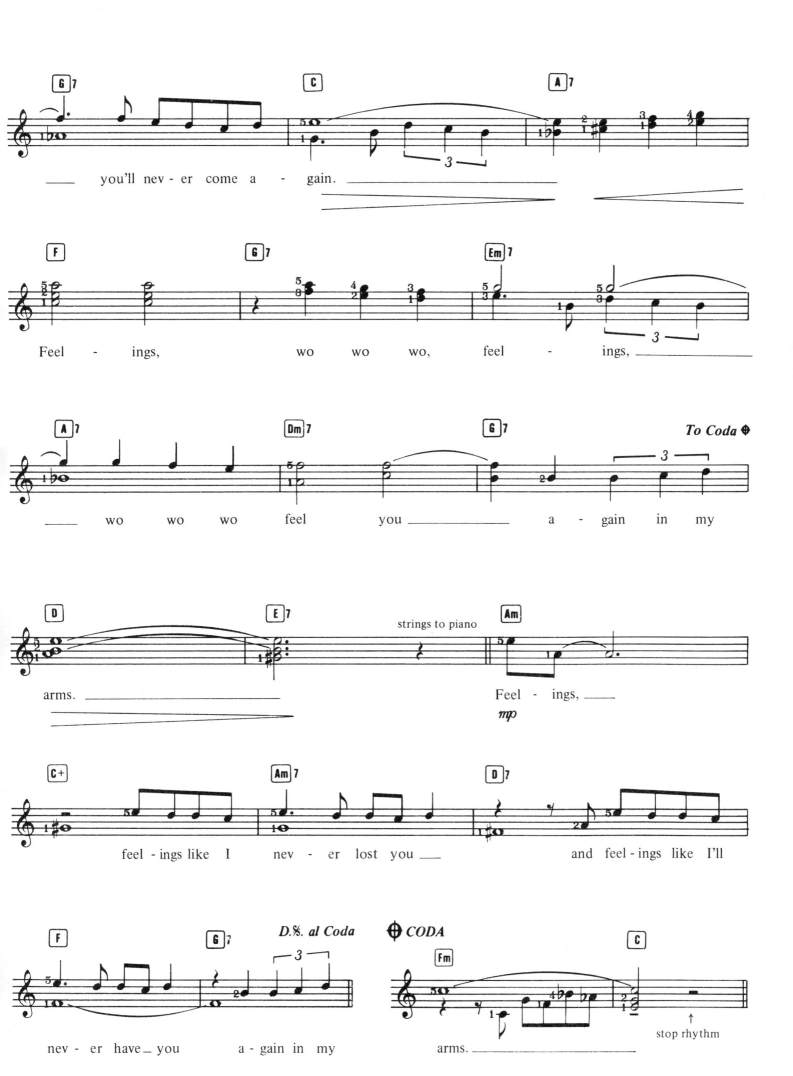

you'll nev - er come a - gain.

Feel - ings, wo wo wo, feel - ings,

wo wo wo feel you a - gain in my

arms. Feel - ings,

feel - ings like I nev - er lost you and feel - ings like I'll

nev - er have you a - gain in my arms.

45

Fernando

WORDS & MUSIC BY BENNY ANDERSSON, STIG ANDERSON & BJORN ULVAEUS

Voice: guitar
Rhythm: rock
Tempo: medium (♩ = 112)

VERSES

Can you hear the drums Fer - nan - do?___ I re - mem - ber long a -
They were clo - ser now, Fer - nan - do.___ Ev - 'ry hour___ ev' - ry

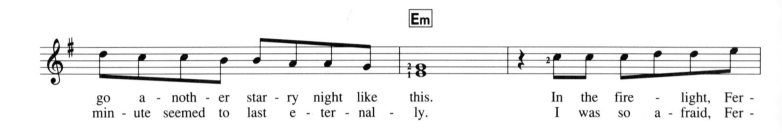

go a - noth - er star - ry night like this. In the fire - light, Fer -
min - ute seemed to last e - ter - nal - ly. I was so a - fraid, Fer -

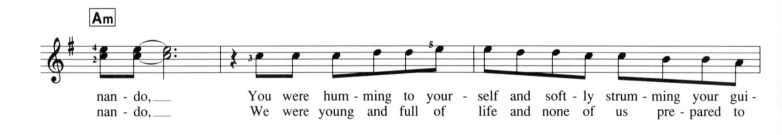

nan - do,___ You were hum - ming to your - self and soft - ly strum - ming your gui -
nan - do,___ We were young and full of life and none of us pre - pared to

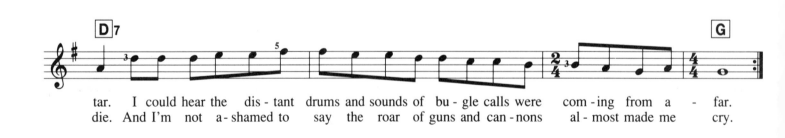

tar. I could hear the dis - tant drums and sounds of bu - gle calls were com - ing from a - far.
die. And I'm not a - shamed to say the roar of guns and can - nons al - most made me cry.

CHORUS

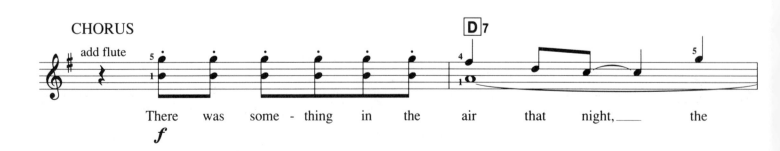

add flute

There was some - thing in the air that night,___ the

f

stars were bright,__ Fer - nan - do.__ They were shin - ing there for

you and me,__ for li - ber - ty,__ Fer - nan - do. Though we

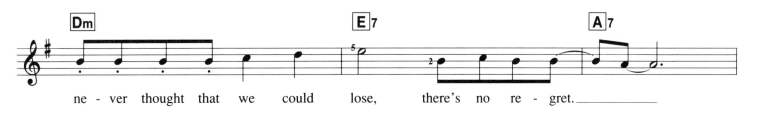

ne - ver thought that we could lose, there's no re - gret.__

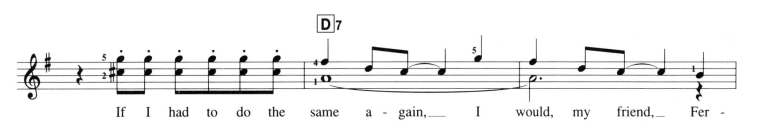

If I had to do the same a - gain,__ I would, my friend,__ Fer -

nan - do.__ If I had to do the same a - gain,__ I

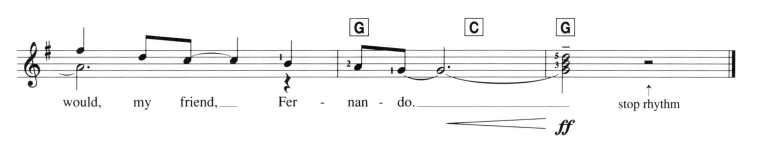

would, my friend,__ Fer - nan - do.__ stop rhythm

ff

Girls And Boys

Words & Music by Damon Albarn, Graham Coxon, Alex James & David Rowntree

Voice: guitar
Rhythm: rock
Tempo: medium (♩ = 120)

Streets like a jun-gle, _____ so call the po-lice. _____

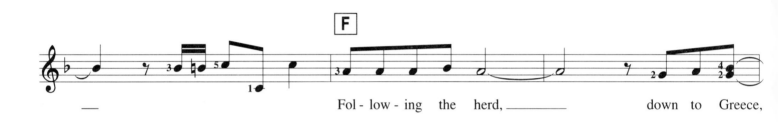

_____ Fol-low-ing the herd, _____ down to Greece,

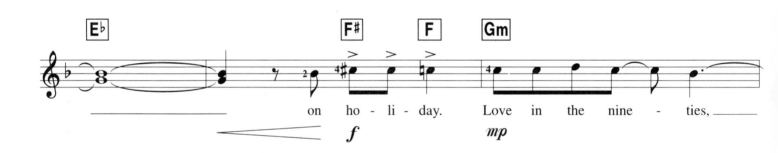

_____ on ho-li-day. Love in the nine-ties, _____

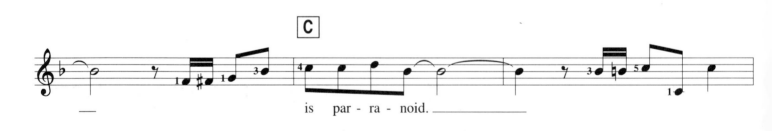

_____ is par-ra-noid. _____

On sun-ny beach-es, _____ take your chan - - -

CHORUS

ces. Look- ing for girls who are boys, who like boys to be girls, who do boys

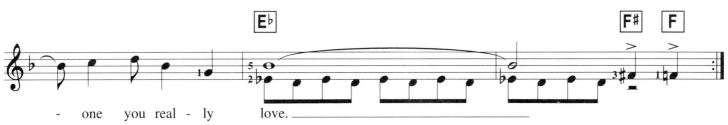

— like they're girls, — who do girls — like they're boys. — Al- ways should — be some-

- one you real - ly love.

INTERLUDE

Oh oh oh oh oh ——— oh. Oh oh oh oh oh. —

mp

D.%. and fade ad lib.

Look - ing for

f

49

DISCO 2000

MUSIC BY PULP | LYRICS BY JARVIS COCKER

Voice: jazz organ
Rhythm: rock
Tempo: fairly fast (♩ = 138)

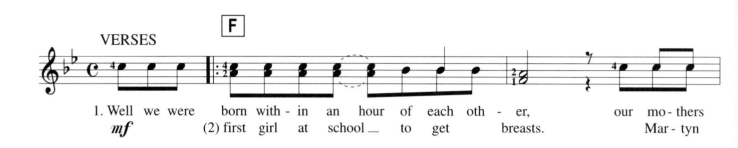

VERSES

1. Well we were born with-in an hour of each oth-er, our mo-thers
mf
(2) first girl at school to get breasts. Mar-tyn

said we could be sis-ter and broth-er, your name is De-bo-rah, De-bo-rah, —
said that yours were the best. The boys all loved you, but I was a mess,

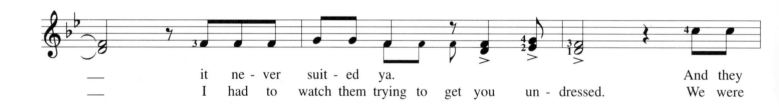

— it ne-ver suit-ed ya. And they
— I had to watch them trying to get you un-dressed. We were

said that when we grew up — we'd get mar-ried, and ne-ver split up.
friends, that was as far as it went. — I — used to walk you home some-times but —

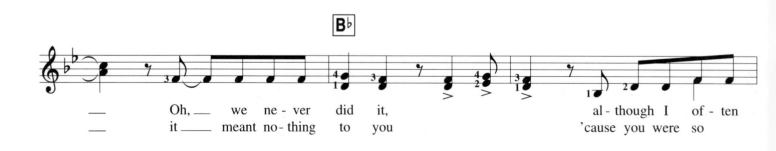

— Oh, — we ne-ver did it, al-though I of-ten
— it — meant no-thing to you 'cause you were so

thought of it. / po - pu - lar. Oh, De - b'rah, do you re - call, ____ your
mp

house was ve - ry small, ____ with wood - chip on the wall, ____ when

I came 'round to call, ____ you did - n't no - tice me at all? ____
cresc.

CHORUS

add trumpet

And I said let's all meet up ____ in the year two - thou - sand,
f

won't it be strange ____ when we're all ful - ly grown, _____ be

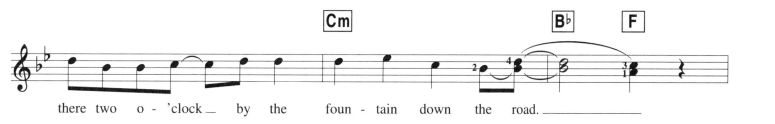

there two o - 'clock ____ by the foun - tain down the road. _____

51

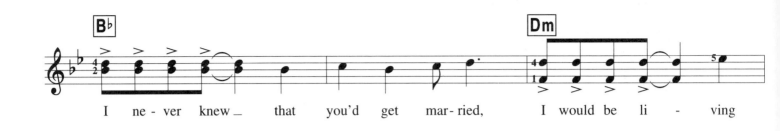

I ne-ver knew __ that you'd get mar-ried, I would be li - ving

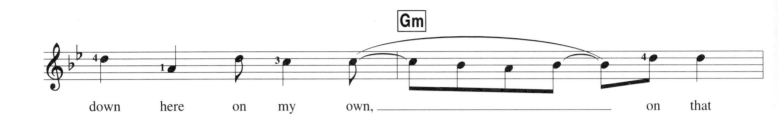

down here on my own, _____ on that

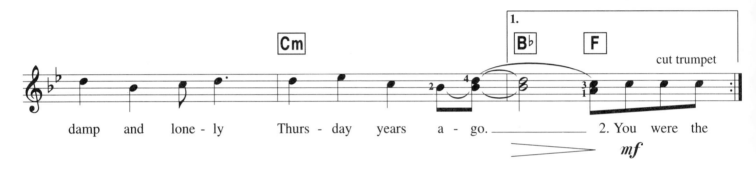

damp and lone-ly Thurs-day years a - go. _____ 2. You were the

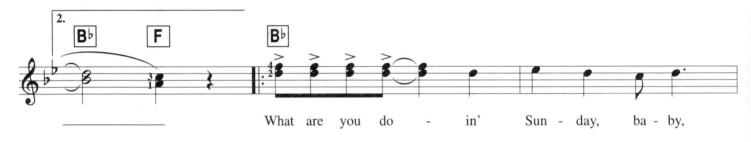

_____ What are you do - in' Sun - day, ba - by,

would you like to come and meet me may-be? You can e - ven bring __

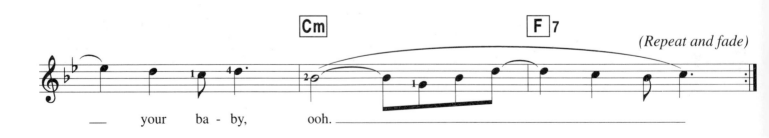

__ your ba - by, ooh. _____

HERO

WORDS & MUSIC BY WALTER AFANASIEFF & MARIAH CAREY

Voice: human voice
Rhythm: 8 beat
Tempo: fairly slow (♩ = 72)

VERSE

1. There's a he - ro ____ if you look in - side your heart, you don't

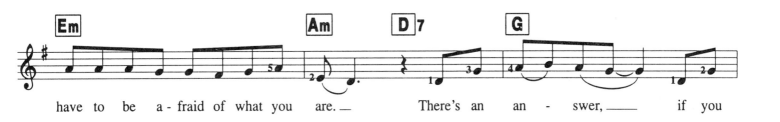

have to be a - fraid of what you are. ____ There's an an - swer, ____ if you

reach in - to your soul, and the sor - row that you know will melt a - way.

add piano

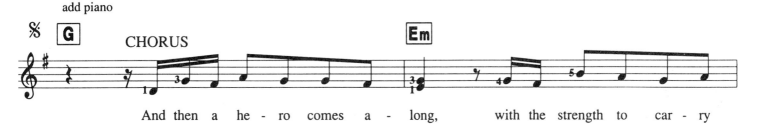

CHORUS

And then a he - ro comes a - long, with the strength to car - ry

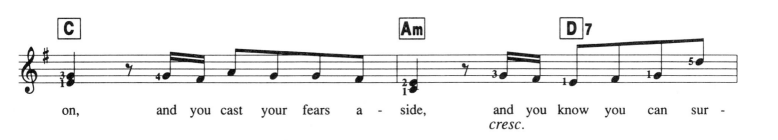

on, and you cast your fears a - side, and you know you can sur -

To Coda ⊕

vive. So when you feel like hope is gone, look in - side you and be

strong, and you fin - 'lly see the truth, that a he - ro lies in
cresc.

cut piano VERSE

you. — 2. It's a long road — when you
f *dim.* *p*

face the world a - lone, no - one reach - es out a hand for you to hold. — You can

find — love —— if you search with - in your - self, and the emp - ti - ness you felt will dis - ap -

add piano
CHORUS

pear. And then a he - ro comes a - long, with the strength to car - ry
mf

on, and you cast your fears a - side, and you know you can sur -

vive. So when you feel like hope is gone, look in-side you and be

strong, and you fin-'lly see the truth, that a he-ro lies in

you. ___
f

Lord ___ knows,
mp

INTERLUDE

dreams are hard to fol-low,
mf

but don't let a-ny-one ___

tear them a-way. ___
mf

Hold ___ on,
mp

D.%.al Coda

there will be to-mor-row, in time you'll find the way.
f

✆ Coda

molto rit.

you, ___
f

stop rhythm

that a he-ro lies in you. ___
ff

Hey Jude

WORDS & MUSIC BY JOHN LENNON & PAUL McCARTNEY

Voice: guitar
Rhythm: rock
Tempo: medium (♩ = 92)
Synchro-start

Hey Jude, don't make it bad, take a
Jude, don't be a - fraid, you were

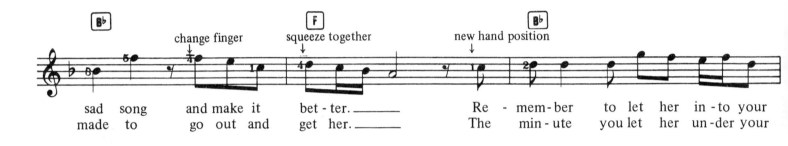

sad song and make it bet - ter. _____ Re - mem - ber to let her in - to your
made to go out and get her. _____ The min - ute you let her un - der your

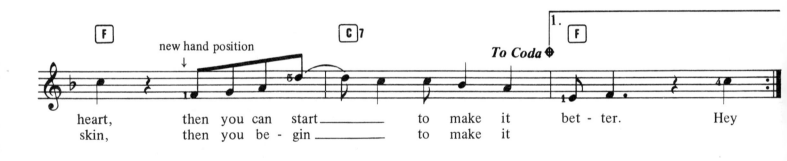

heart, then you can start _____ to make it bet - ter. Hey
skin, then you be - gin _____ to make it

bet - ter. _____ And an - y - time you feel the pain, hey Jude _____ re -

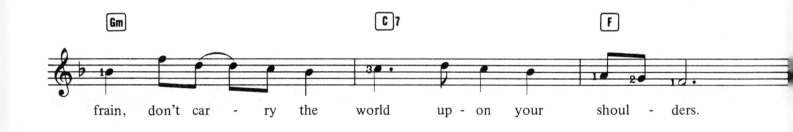

frain, don't car - ry the world up - on your shoul - ders.

For now you know that it's a fool who plays—— it cool by mak - ing his

world a lit - tle cold - er. Da da da da da da da da

D.%. al Coda

⊕ *CODA*

da. Hey

mf

bet - ter, bet -ter, bet - ter, bet-ter,

bet - ter, bet - ter, Oh! Da da da da da da da,

f *p*

new hand position

da da da da, Hey—— Jude. Da da da

f *p*

da da da da, da da da da, Hey—— Jude.

f

* high F

I Believe

Words & Music by Ervin Drake, Irvin Graham, Jimmy Shirl & Al Stillman

Voice: piano
Rhythm: slow rock
Tempo: slow (♩ = 72)

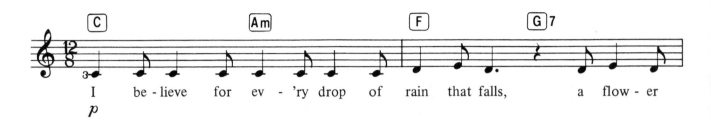

I be-lieve for ev-'ry drop of rain that falls, a flow-er

p

grows. _____ I be-lieve that some-where in the

dark-est night, a can-dle glows. _____

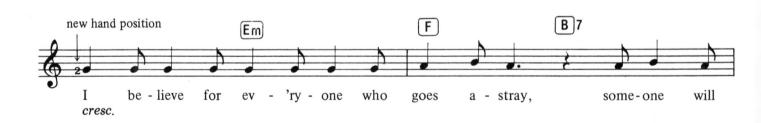

I be-lieve for ev-'ry-one who goes a-stray, some-one will

cresc.

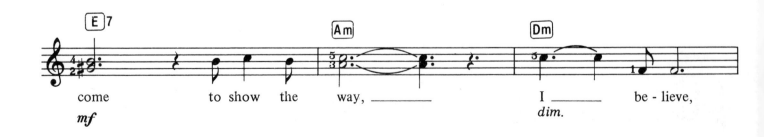

come to show the way, _____ I _____ be-lieve,

mf *dim.*

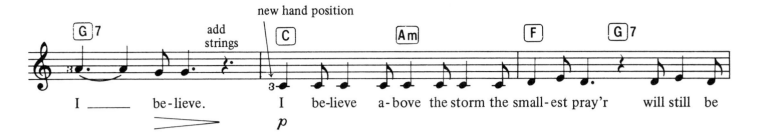

I _____ be-lieve. I be-lieve a-bove the storm the small-est pray'r will still be

heard. _____ I be - lieve that some - one in the

great some-where hears ev - 'ry word. _____

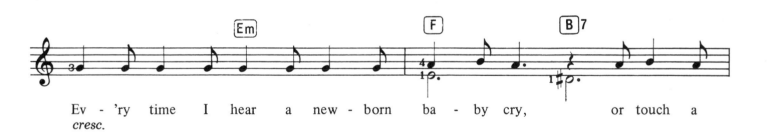

Ev - 'ry time I hear a new-born ba - by cry, or touch a
cresc.

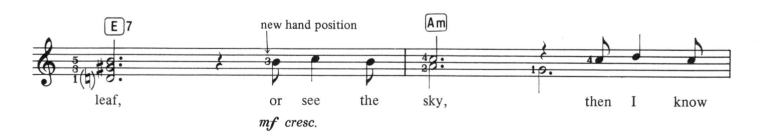

leaf, or see the sky, then I know
mf cresc.

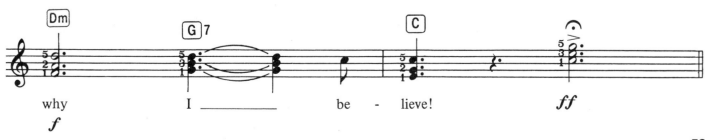

why I _____ be - lieve! *ff*
f

I Know Him So Well

WORDS & MUSIC BY BENNY ANDERSSON, TIM RICE & BJORN ULVAEUS

Voice: string ensemble
Rhythm: rock
Tempo: slow (♩ = 76)

No-thing is so good it lasts e - ter-nal-y. Per-fect sit - u - a -tions must go

wrong. But this has nev - er yet pre - ven-ted me

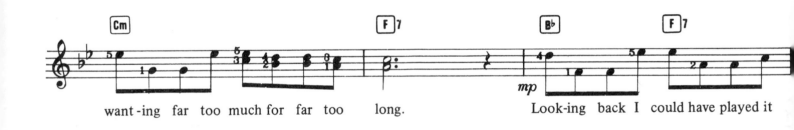

want -ing far too much for far too long. Look-ing back I could have played it

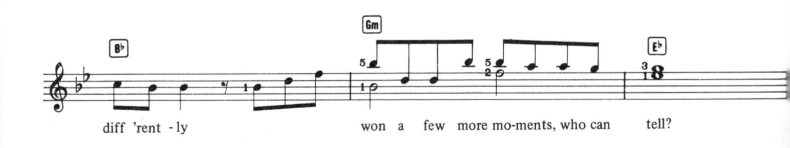

diff 'rent -ly won a few more mo-ments, who can tell?

But it took time to un - der -stand the man, now at least I know I know him

CHORUS

well. Was-n't it good? Was-n't it fine? Is-n't it

mad-ness, he can't be mine? _____ But in the end he needs a lit-tle bit
cresc.

more than me, more _____ se - cu - ri - ty, his fan-ta-sy and free-dom, I know him so
f

well. _____ *p*

CODA

_____ But
cresc.

in the end he needs a lit-tle bit more than me, more _____ se - cu - ri -ty, his fan-ta-sy and
f *mf*

free - dom, I know him so _____ well. *f* stop rhythm

I Wonder Why

Words & Music by Curtis Stigers & Glen Ballard

Voice: flute
Rhythm: waltz
Tempo: medium (♩ = 95)

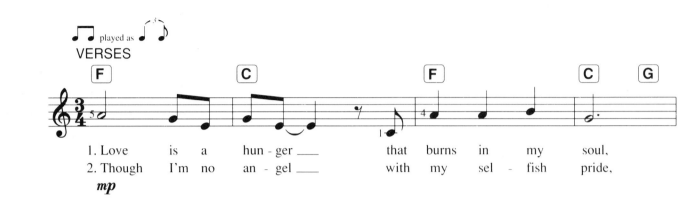

1. Love is a hun - ger ____ that burns in my soul,
2. Though I'm no an - gel ____ with my sel - fish pride,

but you've ne - ver no - ticed ____ the pain. ____ And
but I love you more ____ e - v'ry day. ____ And

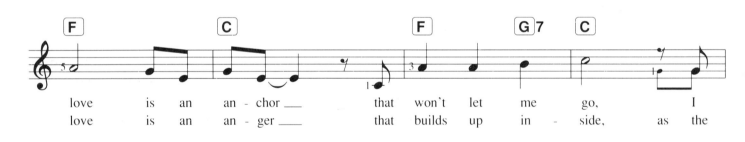

love is an an - chor ____ that won't let me go, I
love is an an - ger ____ that builds up in - side, as the

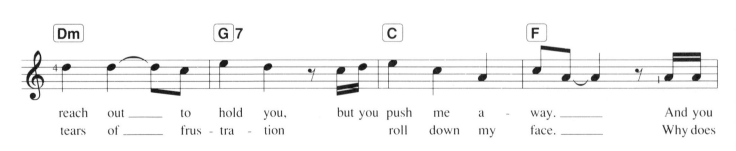

reach out ____ to hold you, but you push me a - way. ____ And you
tears of ____ frus - tra - tion roll down my face. ____ Why does

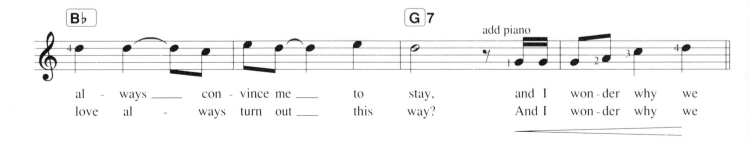

al - ways ____ con - vince me ____ to stay, and I won - der why we
love al - ways turn out ____ this way? And I won - der why we

CHORUS

hold on _____ with tears in our eyes, and I won-der why we have to
hold on _____ with tears in our eyes, and I won-der why we have to

break down ____ to make things all right. And I won-der why I
break down ____ to just make things right. And I won-der why I

can't seem _____ to tell you good - bye. _____ Yeah, I
can't seem _____ to tell you good - bye. _____ Oh, I

INTERLUDE

cut piano
(1st time only)

won-der why. _____
won-der why. _____

I don't want to fight a - gain to - night a - bout the

mp

lit - tle things, ___ please ba - by. I just want to find my way back to

cresc.

D.S. and fade

love, _____ oh, and I'll meet you there, and I won-der why we

f

63

I'll Never Fall In Love Again

Words by Hal David | Music by Burt Bacharach

Voice: synth
Rhythm: disco
Tempo: medium (♩ = 104)

What do you get when you fall in love,— a girl with a pin to burst—
What do you get when you kiss a girl,— you get e-nough germs to catch—

mp

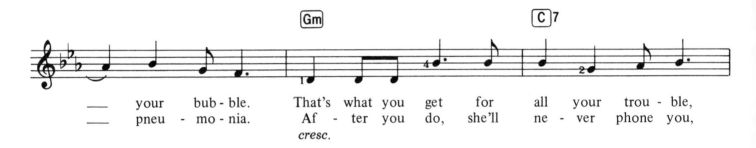

— your bub-ble. That's what you get for all your trou-ble,
— pneu-mo-nia. Af-ter you do, she'll ne-ver phone you,

cresc.

I'll   ne-ver fall in love a-gain. _____
I'll   ne-ver fall in love a-gain. _____

mf

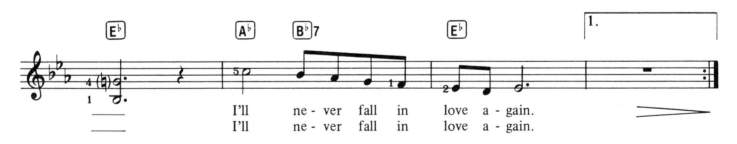

1.

__ I'll ne-ver fall in love a-gain.
__ I'll ne-ver fall in love a-gain.

2.

synth. to strings

Don't tell me what it's all a-bout,— 'cause

mp

I've been there __ and I'm glad I'm out, _____ out of those chains, those

cresc.

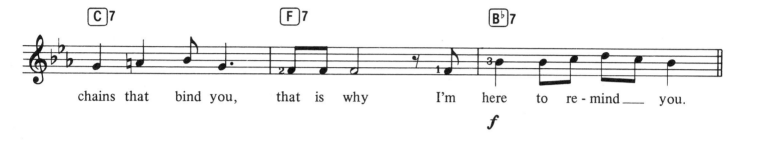

chains that bind you, that is why I'm here to re-mind __ you.

f

strings to synth.

What do you get when you fall in love, __ you on-ly get lies and pain __

mf

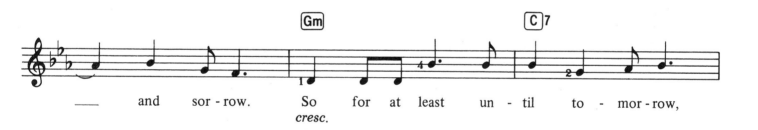

__ and sor-row. So for at least un-til to-mor-row,

cresc.

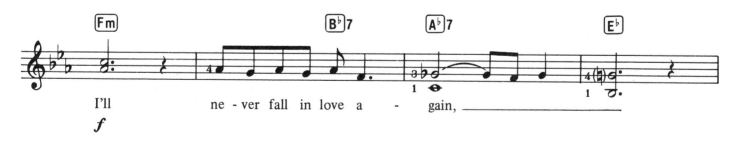

I'll ne-ver fall in love a - gain, _____

f

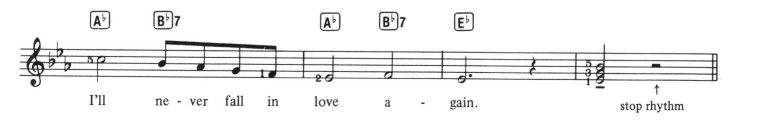

I'll ne-ver fall in love a - gain.

stop rhythm

65

I'm Every Woman
Words & Music by Nickolas Ashford & Valerie Simpson

Voice: guitar
Rhythm: disco
Tempo: medium (♩ = 108)

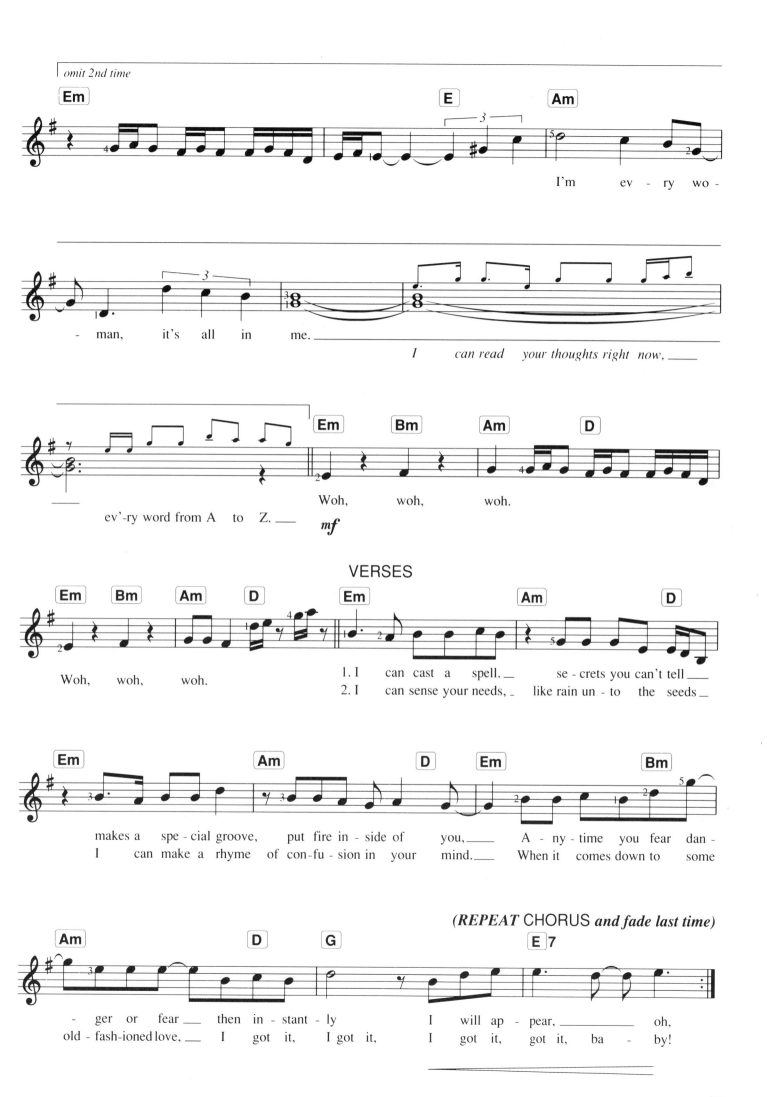

If I Ever Lose My Faith In You

Words & Music by Sting

Voice: guitar
Rhythm: 8 beat
Tempo: fairly slow (♩ = 88)

VERSES

mp
1. You could say I lost my faith in sci-ence and pro-gress.
2. Some would say I was a lost man in a lost world.
3. Ne-ver saw no mi-ra-cle of sci-ence

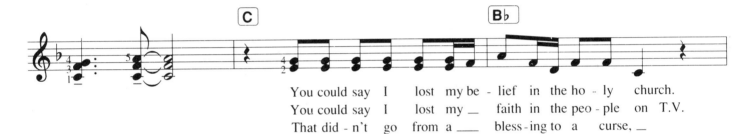

You could say I lost my be-lief in the ho-ly church.
You could say I lost my faith in the peo-ple on T.V.
That did-n't go from a bless-ing to a curse,

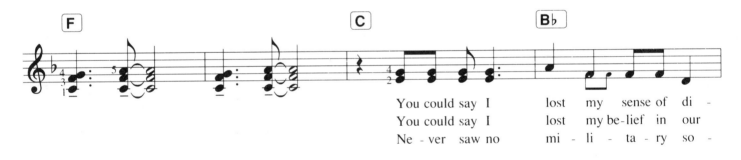

You could say I lost my sense of di -
You could say I lost my be-lief in our
Ne-ver saw no mi-li-ta-ry so -

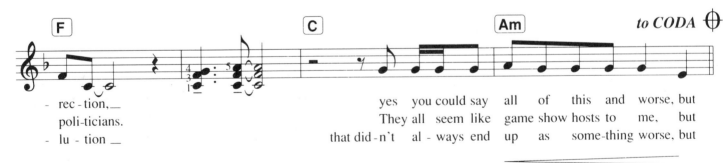

to CODA

- rec-tion, yes you could say all of this and worse, but
poli-ticians. They all seem like game show hosts to me, but
- lu-tion that did-n't al-ways end up as some-thing worse, but

CHORUS

add brass
if I e-ver lose my faith in you,

mf

68

there'd be no-thing left ___ for _ me __ to do. ___

BRIDGE

I could be lost in - side their lies, _____ with

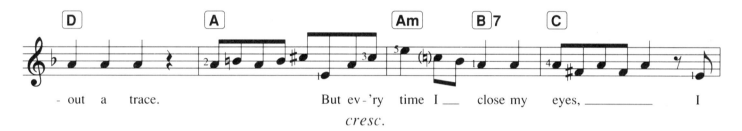

- out a trace. But ev-'ry time I __ close my eyes, _____ I

D. S. al CODA   **CODA**

see your face. _____   if I e - ver lose __ my faith, _   if I e - ver lose _

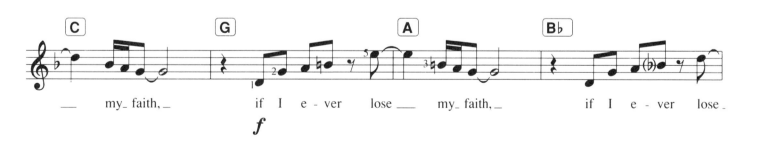

__ my_ faith, _   if I e - ver lose __ my_ faith, _   if I e - ver lose _

__ my _ faith _____   in you._ _____   In you _

69

If Not For You

Words & Music by Bob Dylan

Voice: clarinet
Rhythm: rock
Tempo: medium (♩ = 108)

If not for you my sky would fall, rain would gath - er too. _

mp

_ With - out your love, I'd be no - where at all.

cresc.

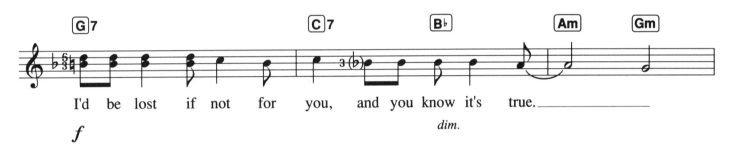

I'd be lost if not for you, and you know it's true. _____

f   *dim.*

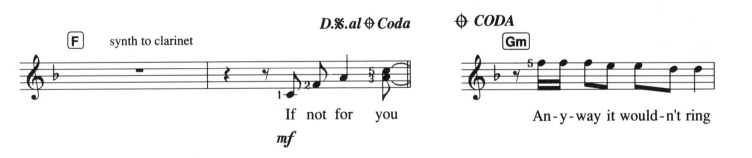

D.%.al ⊕ Coda   ⊕ CODA

synth to clarinet

If not for you   An - y - way it would - n't ring

mf

true, _____   if not ___ for you. _____

(Repeat and fade)

If not for you. _____   If not for you.

Just The Two Of Us

Words & Music by Ralph MacDonald, William Salter & Bill Withers

Voice: electric piano
Rhythm: latin (e.g., samba, bossa nova)
Tempo: fast (♩ = 192)

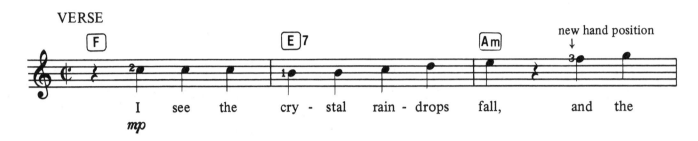

I see the cry - stal rain - drops fall, and the

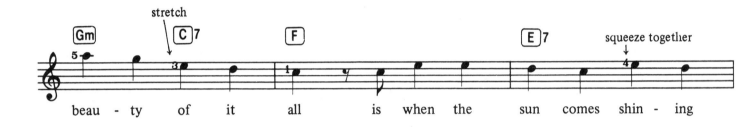

beau - ty of it all is when the sun comes shin - ing

through. _____ To make those

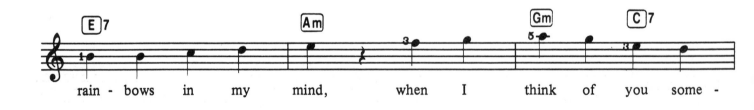

rain - bows in my mind, when I think of you some -

time, and I want to spend ___ some-time with you. _____

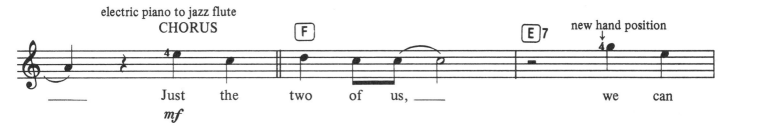

Just the two of us, ___ we can

make it if we try, ___ just the two of us, ___

___ just the two of us. ___ Just the

two of us, ___ build - ing cast - les in the sky, ___

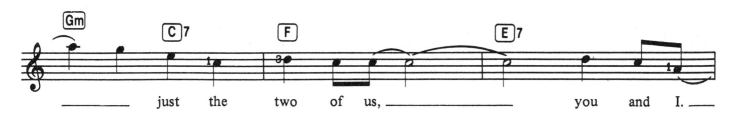

_____ just the two of us, _____ you and I. ___

Lady Madonna

WORDS & MUSIC BY JOHN LENNON & PAUL MCCARTNEY

Voice: harpsichord (with sustain)
Rhythm: rock
Tempo: medium (♩ = 104)

La - dy Ma - don - na,

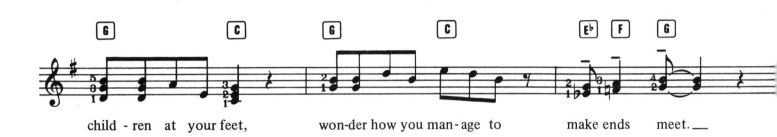

child - ren at your feet, won - der how you man - age to make ends meet.

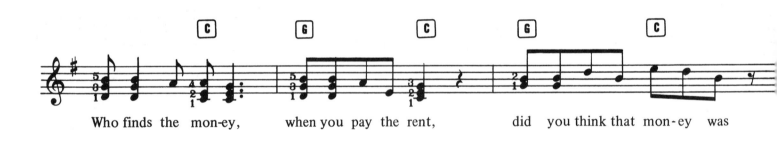

Who finds the mon - ey, when you pay the rent, did you think that mon - ey was

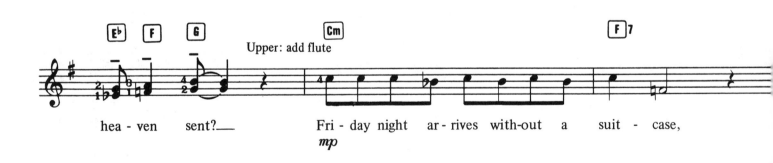

Upper: add flute

hea - ven sent? Fri - day night ar - rives with - out a suit - case,

Sun - day morn - ing creep in like a nun. Mon - day's child has learned to tie his

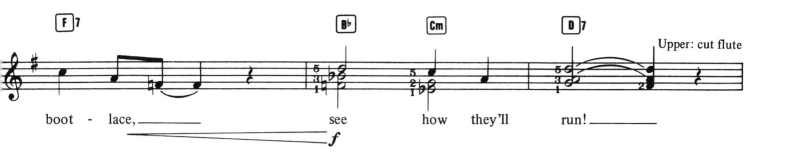

boot - lace, _____ see how they'll run! _____

f

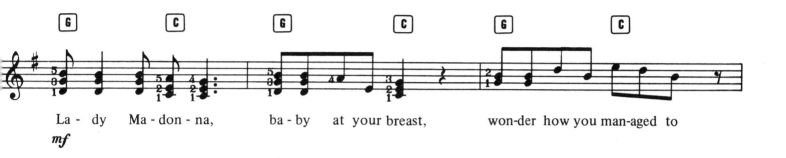

La - dy Ma - don - na, ba - by at your breast, won-der how you man-aged to

mf

feed the ___ rest. La - dy Ma - don - na, ly - ing on the bed,

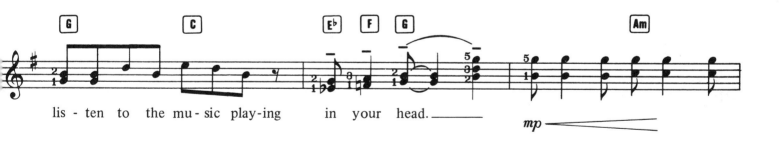

lis - ten to the mu - sic play-ing in your head. _____

mp

mp _____ *mf*

75

Love Me Tender

WORDS & MUSIC BY ELVIS PRESLEY & VERA MATSON

Voice: vibraphone
Rhythm: swing
Tempo: quite slow (♩ = 92)

1. Love me ten - der, love me sweet; ne - ver let me
2. Love me ten - der, love me long; take me to your

p

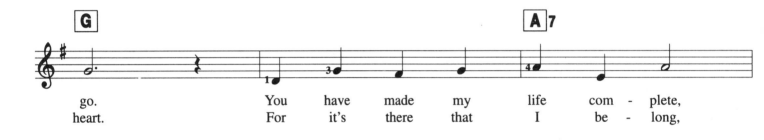

go. You have made my life com - plete,
heart. For it's there that I be - long,

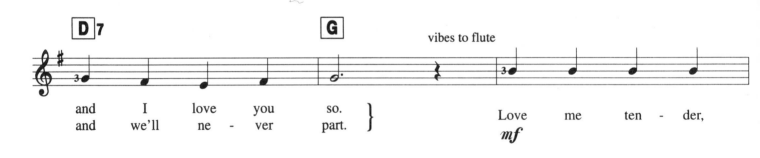

vibes to flute

and I love you so.
and we'll ne - ver part. } Love me ten - der,

mf

love me true, all my dreams ful - fil. For, my dar - lin',

1. flute to vibes
2. flute to strings

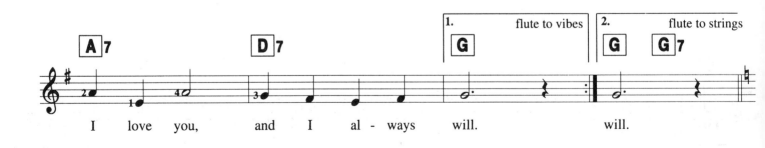

I love you, and I al - ways will. will.

3. Love me ten - der, love me dear; tell me you are
4. When at last, my dreams come true, dar - ling, this I

mine. I'll be yours through all the years,
know: hap - pi - ness through will fol - low you,

till the end of time.
ev - 'ry - where you go.

add piano

Love me ten - der,

love me true, all my dreams ful - fil.

For, my dar - lin', I love you, and I al - ways

cut piano

will. and I al - ways will. stop rhythm

77

Massachusetts

WORDS & MUSIC BY BARRY GIBB, ROBIN GIBB & MAURICE GIBB

Voice: clarinet
Rhythm: rock
Tempo: medium ($\quarternote$ = 92)

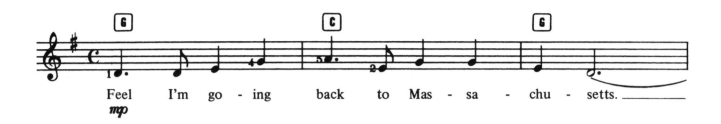

Feel I'm go - ing back to Mas - sa - chu - setts. _____

_____ Some - thing's tell - ing me I must go

home. _____ And the lights all went

out in Mas - sa - chu - setts, the day I

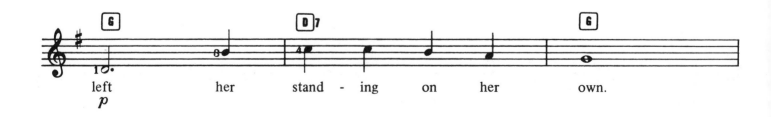

left her stand - ing on her own.

Tried to hitch a ride to San Fran-

mp

cis - co. _____ Got - ta do the

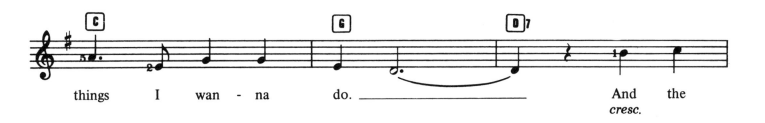

things I wan - na do. _____ And the

cresc.

lights all went out in Mas - sa - chu - setts, they brought me

mf *dim.*

back to see my way with you. They brought me

p *cresc.*

back to see my way with you. stop rhythm

mf

79

MY LOVE
WORDS & MUSIC BY MCCARTNEY

Voice: vibraphone
Rhythm: 8 beat
Tempo: slow (♩ = 76)

1. And when I go a - way,   I know my heart can stay with my   love, ___ it's un - der-
3. Don't e - ver ask me why   I ne - ver say good - bye to my   love, ___ it's un - der-

stood.   It's in the hands of my love,   and my love does it   good,
stood.   It's ev - 'ry - where with my love,   and my love does it   good,

___   wo - wo wo - wo,   wo - wo wo - wo,
___   wo - wo wo - wo,   wo - wo wo - wo,

To Coda ⊕

my love does it good. ___
my love does it good. ___   2. And when the cup - board's bare,

I'll still find some - thing there with my   love, ___ it's un - der - stood. It's ev - 'ry - where with my

ROCKET MAN
WORDS & MUSIC BY ELTON JOHN & BERNIE TAUPIN

Voice: brass ensemble or brass synthesizer + arpeggio if available
Rhythm: 16 beat (or rock)
Tempo: slow (♩ = 66)

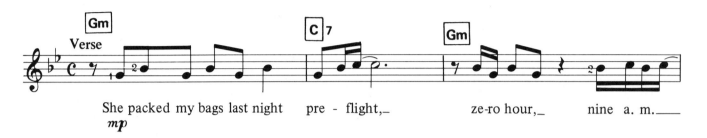

She packed my bags last night pre - flight,_ ze-ro hour,_ nine a. m._

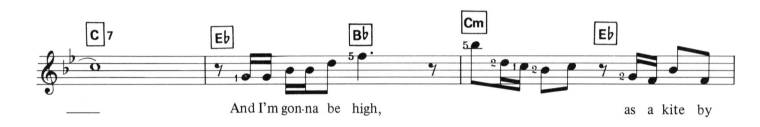

_ And I'm gon-na be high, as a kite by

then. I miss the earth so much, I

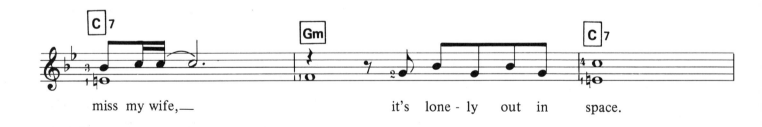

miss my wife,_ it's lone - ly out in space.

On such a time_____ less flight._

ROMEO AND JULIET

WORDS & MUSIC BY MARK KNOPFLER

Voice: guitar, to piano, to flute
Rhythm: 8 beat
Tempo: fairly slow (♩ = 84)

VERSES

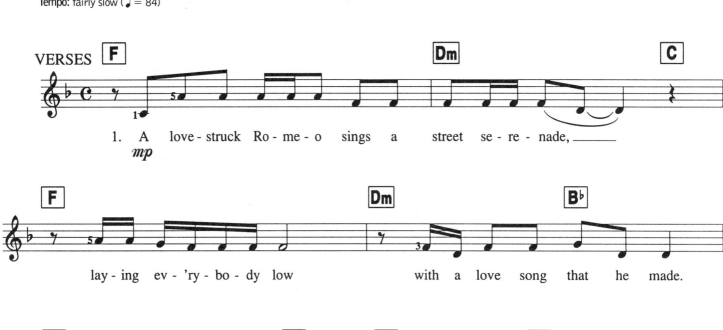

1. A love-struck Ro-me-o sings a street se-re-nade, _____
mp
lay-ing ev-'ry-bo-dy low with a love song that he made.

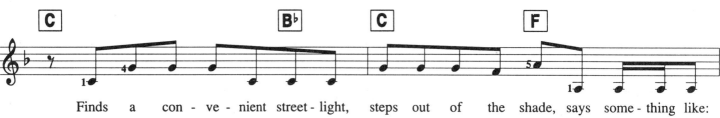

Finds a con-ve-nient street-light, steps out of the shade, says some-thing like:

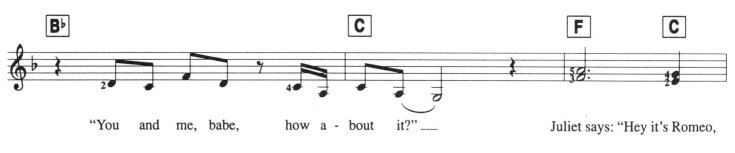

"You and me, babe, how a-bout it?" ___ Juliet says: "Hey it's Romeo,

you nearly gave me a He's un-der-neath the win-dow, she's sing-ing, "Hey la, my boy-friend's back.
heart attack."

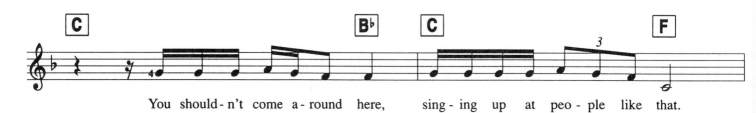

You should-n't come a-round here, sing-ing up at peo-ple like that.

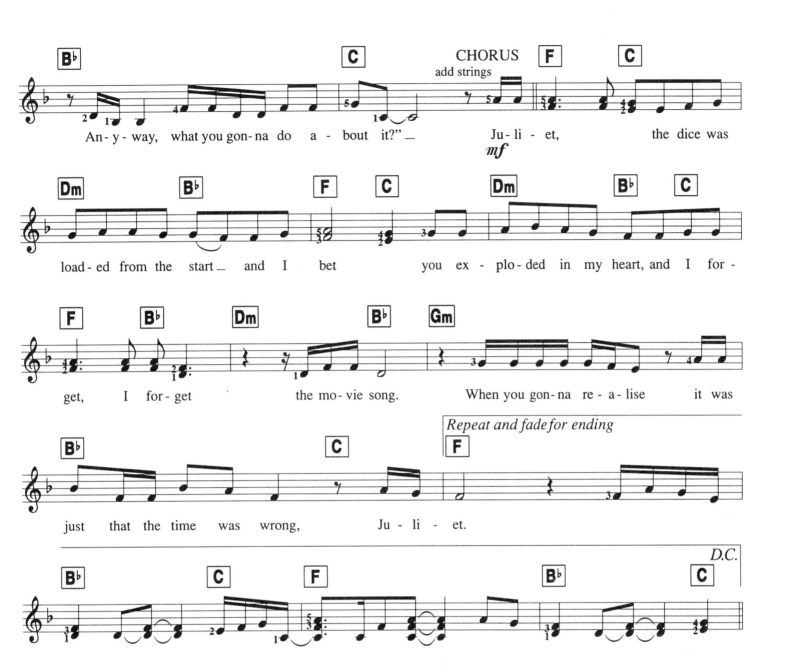

An-y-way, what you gon-na do a-bout it?" — Ju-li-et, the dice was
load-ed from the start — and I bet you ex-plo-ded in my heart, and I for-
get, I for-get the mo-vie song. When you gon-na re-a-lise it was
just that the time was wrong, Ju-li-et.

Repeat and fade for ending

D.C.

Verse 2:   Come up on different streets
They both were streets of shame.
Both dirty, both mean,
Yes and the dream was just the same.
And I dreamed your dream for you
And now your dream is real.
How can you look at me
As if I was just another one of your deals.

When you can fall for chains of silver
You can fall for chains of gold
You can fall for pretty strangers
And the promises they hold.
You promised me everything,
You promised me thick and thin
Now you just say oh Romeo, yeah,
You know I used to have a scene with him.

Chorus 2:   Juliet, when we made love you used to cry
You said I love you like the stars above,
I'll love you till I die.
There's a place for us
You know the movie song,
When you gonna realise
It was just that the time was wrong,
Juliet?

Verse 3:   I can't do the talk
Like they talk on T.V.
And I can't do a love song
Like the way it's meant to be.
I can't do everything
But I'd do anything for you
I can't do anything
Except be in love with you.

And all I do is miss you
And the way we used to be
All I do is keep the beat
And bad company.
All I do is kiss you
Through the bars of a rhyme
Julie I'd do the stars
With you any time.

Chorus 3:   Juliet, when we made love you used to cry
You said I love you like the stars above,
I'll love you till I die.
And there's a place for us
You know the movie song,
When you gonna realise
It was just that the time was wrong,
Juliet?

Sacrifice
WORDS & MUSIC BY ELTON JOHN & BERNIE TAUPIN

Voice: string ensemble
Rhythm: 8 beat
Tempo: medium (♩ = 100)

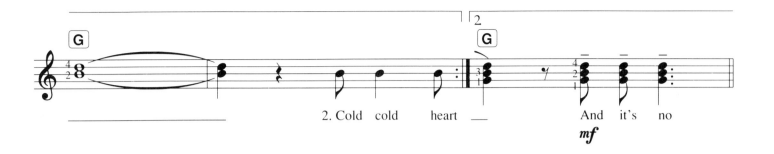

2. Cold cold heart __ And it's no

CHORUS

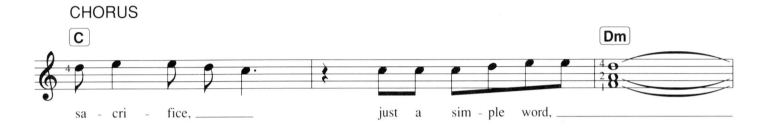

sa - cri - fice, _____ just a sim - ple word, _____

__ it's two hearts li - ving __ in two se - pa - rate worlds.

_____ But it's no sa - cri - fice, _____

__ no sa - cri - fice, _____ it's no sa -

- cri - fice _____ at _____ all. __

Satin Doll

Words by Johnny Mercer | Music by Duke Ellington & Billy Strayhorn

Voice: vibes (with sustain)
Rhythm: swing
Tempo: medium (♩ = 108)

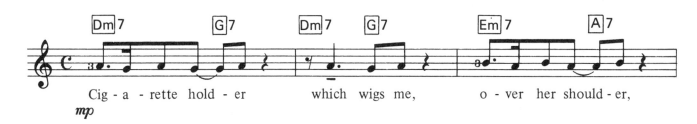

Cig - a - rette hold - er which wigs me, o - ver her should - er,

mp

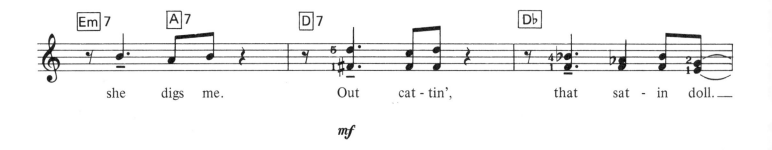

she digs me. Out cat - tin', that sat - in doll.

mf

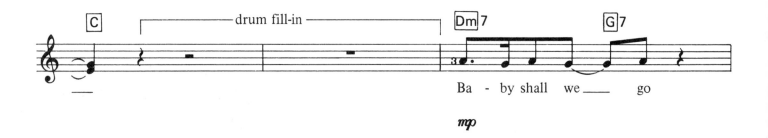

Ba - by shall we go

mp

out skip - pin', care - ful a - mi - go, you're flip - pin',

speaks Lat - in, that sat - in doll

mf

add trumpet | **Gm**7 | **C**7 | **Gm**7 | **C**7

She's no-bo-dy's fool,— so I'm play - ing it cool — as can be.
mp

F | | | **Am**7 | **D**7

I'll give it a whirl,— but I ain't —
cresc.

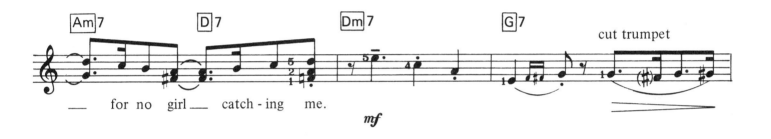

Am7 | **D**7 | **Dm**7 | **G**7 | cut trumpet

— for no girl — catch-ing me.
mf

Dm7 | **G**7 | **Dm**7 | **G**7 | **Em**7 | **A**7 | **Em**7 | **A**7

Tel - e - phone num - bers, well, you know, do-ing my rhum - bas, with u - no,
mp

D7 | **Db** | **C** | drum fill-in

and that 'n', my sat - in doll. —
mf

D7 | **Db** | **C** N.C. | **C**

And that - 'n', my sat - in doll. stop rhythm cut chord
f

89

Saviour's Day
Words & Music by Chris Eaton

Voice: oboe (reed)
Rhythm: waltz
Tempo: fast (♩ = 126)

VERSES

1. Now we have been through the har- vest, _____ win- ter has
2. Ma - ny have come from the val - leys, _____ ma - ny have
3. Join - ing the old and the young ones, _____ join - ing the
4. Here's to the God of the pre - sent, _____ here's to the

tru - ly be - gun. _____ Now we are walk - ing the
come from the hills. _____ Ma - ny have start - ed their
black and the white. _____ Meet - ing the need of the
God of the past. _____ Here's to the hope and the

chill of the night, we are wait - ing for, wait - ing for _____
jour - ney home, to be with some- one, with some - one _____
hun - gry is He, will we ev - er re - mem - ber Him, _____
fu - ture He brings, we will sing to Him, sing to Him, _____

1, 3.

for the Sa - viour's Day.
on the Sa - viour's
on the Sa - viour's Day.
on the Sa - viour's

2, 4.

Day.
Day.

90

CHORUS

O - pen your eyes on Sa - viour's Day. Don't look back or turn a - way. Life can be yours if you on - ly stay. He is call - ing you, call - ing you, on the Sa - viour's Day.

add strings

dim.

D.C.(Verse 3)
cut strings

So Far Away

WORDS & MUSIC BY MARK KNOPFLER

Voice: guitar
Rhythm: rock
Tempo: medium (♩ = 108)

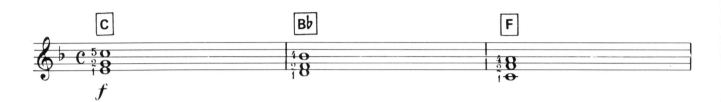

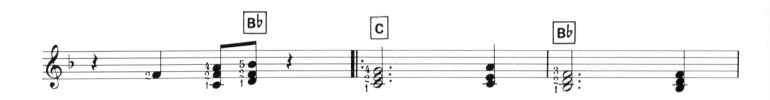

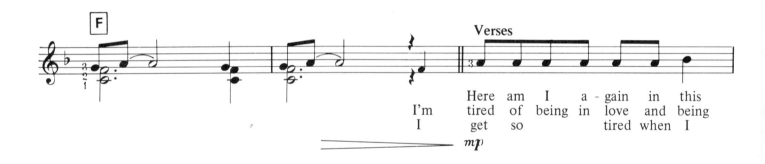

Verses

Here am I a - gain in this
I'm tired of being in love and being
I get so tired when I

mean old town,__ and you're so far a - way____ from me. Now
all a - lone,__ when you're so far a - way____ from me. I'm
have to ex-plain,__ when you're so far a - way____ from me. See,

where are you when the sun goes down,__ you're so far a - way__
tired of making out on the tel - e - phone,__ 'cause you're so far a - way__
you've been in the sun and I've been in the rain, and you're so far a - way__

Chorus
add synth

_____ from me.
_____ from me.
_____ from me.

You're so far a - way from me,_____

_mf_

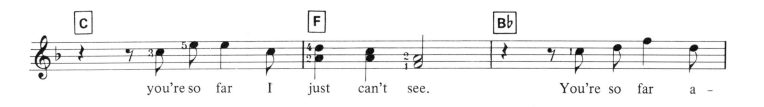

you're so far I just can't see.   You're so far a -

way   from me,_____   you're   so   far   a - way_____   from

(Repeat twice)

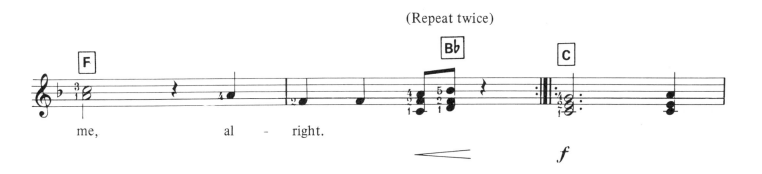

me,   al - right.

_f_

(Repeat & Fade)

93

Something

WORDS & MUSIC BY GEORGE HARRISON

Voice: brass ensemble + rock guitar
Rhythm: rock
Tempo: slow (♩ = 76)

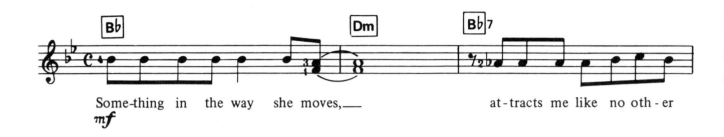

Some-thing in the way she moves,⎯ at-tracts me like no oth-er

mf

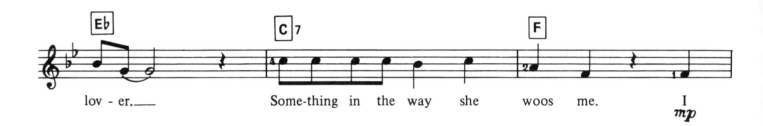

lov - er.⎯ Some-thing in the way she woos me. I

mp

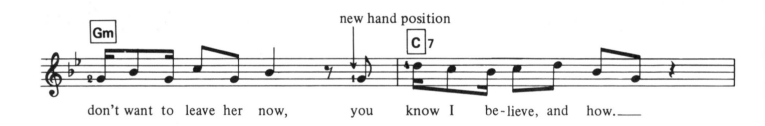

new hand position

don't want to leave her now, you know I be-lieve, and how.⎯

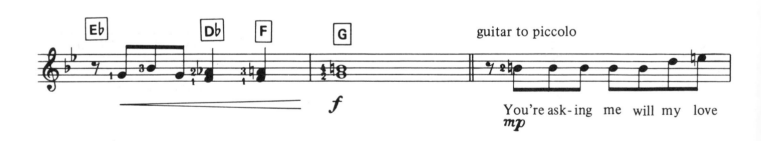

guitar to piccolo

f

You're ask-ing me will my love

mp

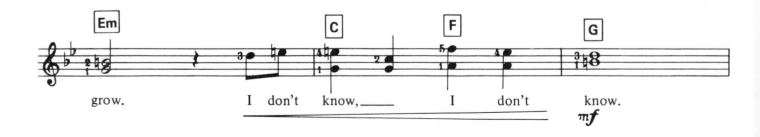

grow. I don't know,⎯ I don't know.

mf

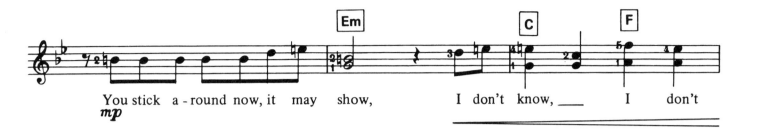

You stick a-round now, it may show, I don't know, ___ I don't

mp

piccolo to rock guitar

know. Some-thing in the way she knows, ___

mf

and all I have to do is think of her. Some-thing in the things she

shows me. I don't want to leave her now, you know I be-lieve, and how, __

mp

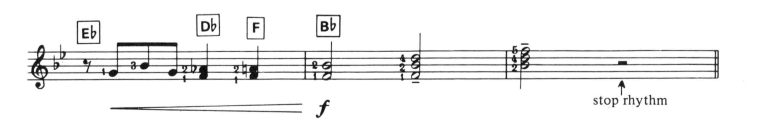

f

stop rhythm

SOMETIMES WHEN WE TOUCH

WORDS & MUSIC BY DAN HILL & BARRY MANN

Voice: electric piano
Rhythm: rock (or bossa nova)
Tempo: slow (♩ = 84)

VERSE

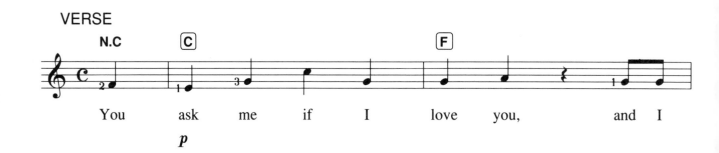

You ask me if I love you, and I

choke on my re - ply. I'd rath - er hurt you

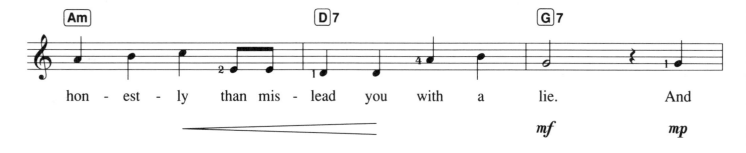

hon - est - ly than mis - lead you with a lie. And

who am I to judge you on what you say or

do? I'm on - ly just be - gin - ning to

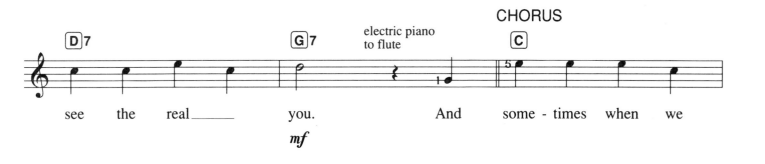

CHORUS

see the real___ you. And some - times when we

touch the hon - est - y's too much. And I

have to close my eyes and hide.___

___ I wan - na hold you till I die, till we

both break down and cry, I wan - na hold you till the

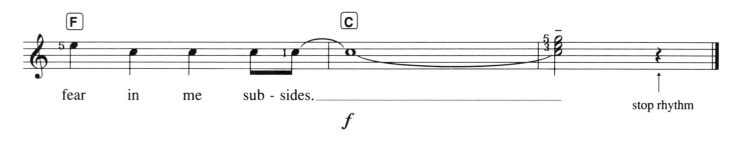

fear in me sub - sides.___

Somewhere Out There

Words & Music by James Horner, Barry Mann & Cynthia Weil

Voice: clarinet
Rhythm: rock
Tempo: medium (♩ = 96)

Some - where   out   there,   be - neath the pale moon -

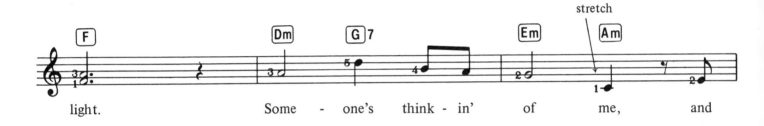

light.   Some - one's think - in' of me,   and

lov - ing me to - night. _____   Some - where _____

out _____ there,   some one's say - ing a   prayer,   that

we'll find one an - oth - er,   in that big some - where ___ out ___

there. And ev - en though I know how ve - ry far a - part we are, ___ it

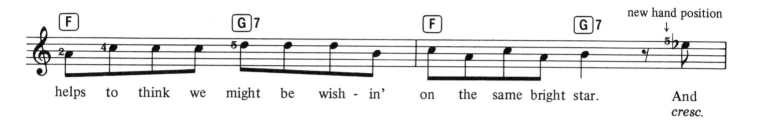

helps to think we might be wish - in' on the same bright star. And

when the night wind starts to sing a lone - some lul - a - by, it

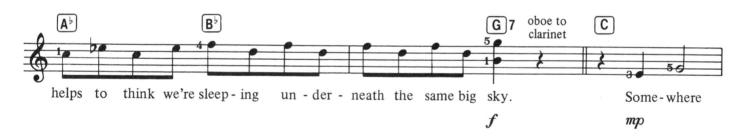

helps to think we're sleep - ing un - der - neath the same big sky. Some - where

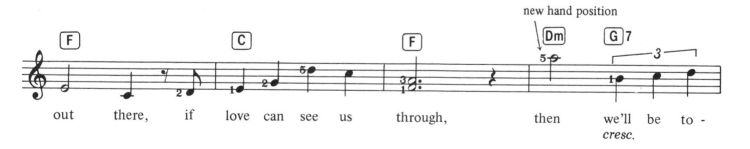

out there, if love can see us through, then we'll be to -

ge - ther some - where out there, out where dreams come true. ___

Streets Of London

Words & Music by Ralph McTell

Voice: string ensemble + arpeggio
Rhythm: bossa nova
Tempo: medium (♩ = 116)

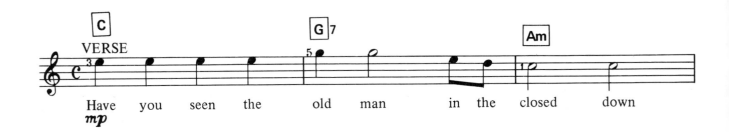

VERSE

Have you seen the old man in the closed down

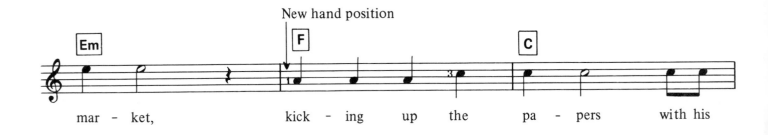

New hand position

mar - ket, kick - ing up the pa - pers with his

new hand position

worn out___ shoes? In his eyes you

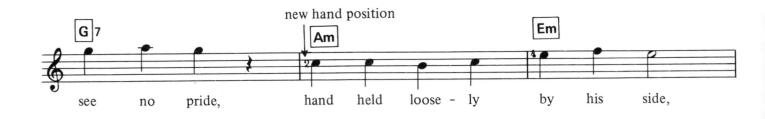

new hand position

see no pride, hand held loose - ly by his side,

new hand position

yes - ter - day's pa - per tell - ing yes - ter - day's

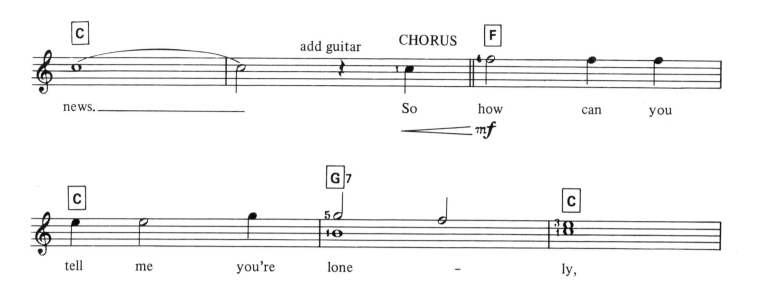

news._____ So how can you

tell me you're lone - ly,

and say for you that the sun don't shine?_____

Let me take you by the hand and

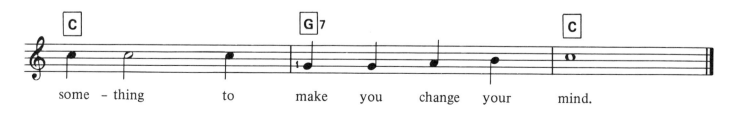

lead you through the streets of Lon - don, I'll show you

some - thing to make you change your mind.

THE SKYE BOAT SONG

TRADITIONAL ARRANGED BY R. WHITTAKER & C. KEYE

Voice: piano
Rhythm: waltz
Tempo: medium (♩ = 88)

CHORUS

INTERLUDE
piano to string ensemble

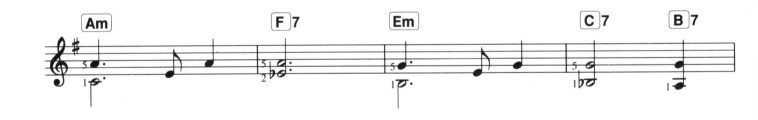

D.C. (with repeat) al FINE

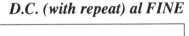

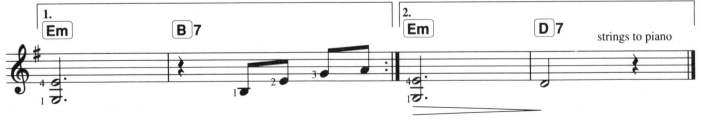

Super Trouper

WORDS & MUSIC BY BENNY ANDERSSON & BJORN ULVAEUS

Voice: human voice
Rhythm: rock
Tempo: medium (♩ = 120)

CHORUS

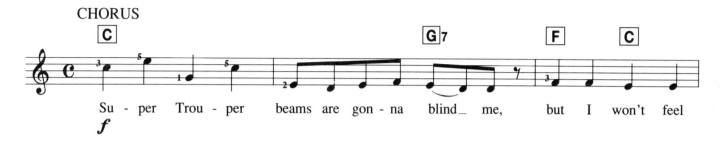

Su - per Trou - per beams are gon - na blind_ me, but I won't feel

blue, like I al - ways do,____ 'cause some - where in the crowd_ there's

INSTRUMENTAL

you.

VERSES

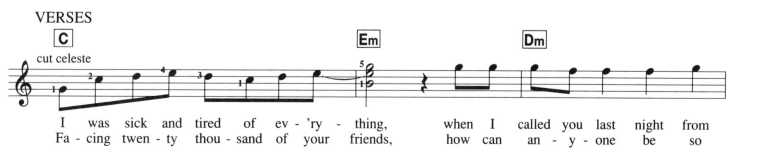

I was sick and tired of ev - 'ry - thing, when I called you last night from
Fa - cing twen - ty thou - sand of your friends, how can an - y - one be so

Glas - gow. / lone - ly?
All I do is eat and sleep and sing, / Part of a suc - cess that ne - ver ends,
wish - ing / still I'm

ev - 'ry show was the last_____ show. / think - ing a - bout you on - ly.
So i - ma - gine I was / There are mo - ments when I

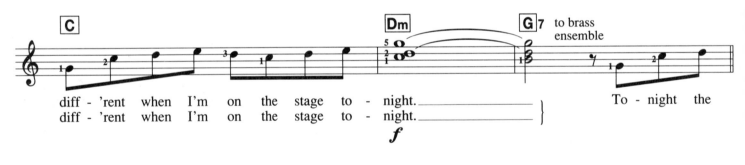

glad to hear you're com - ing, / think I'm go - ing cra - zy,
sud - den - ly I feel al - right, / but it's gon - na be al - right.
and it's gon - na be so / Ev - 'ry thing will be so

cresc.

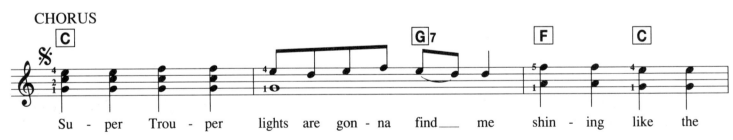

diff - 'rent when I'm on the stage to - night._____ / diff - 'rent when I'm on the stage to - night._____
f
to brass ensemble

To - night the

CHORUS

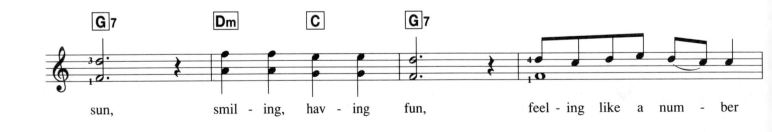

Su - per Trou - per lights are gon - na find_____ me shin - ing like the

sun, smil - ing, hav - ing fun, feel - ing like a num - ber

104

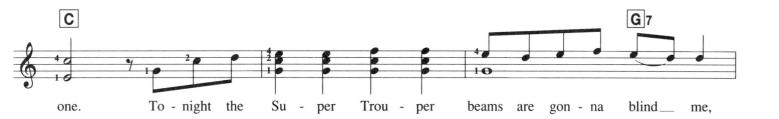

one. To - night the Su - per Trou - per beams are gon - na blind___ me,

but I won't feel blue, like I al - ways

do, 'cause some - where in the crowd___ there's you.___

INTERLUDE

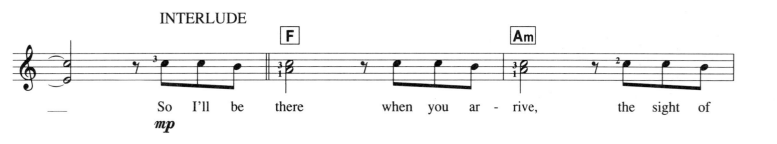

___ So I'll be there when you ar - rive, the sight of
mp

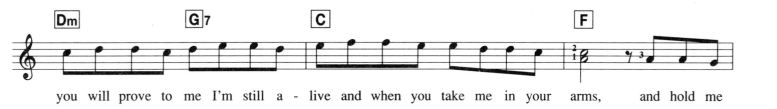

you will prove to me I'm still a - live and when you take me in your arms, and hold me

tight, I know it's gon - na mean so much to - night.___ To - night the
cresc. *f*

Superstar

WORDS & MUSIC BY LEON RUSSELL & BONNIE BRAMLETT

Voice: clarinet
Rhythm: rock
Tempo: fairly slow (♩ = 88)

Verses

Long a - go, and, oh so far a - way,
Lone - li - ness is such a sad af - fair,

mp

___ I fell in love with you, be - fore the
and I can hard - ly wait to be with

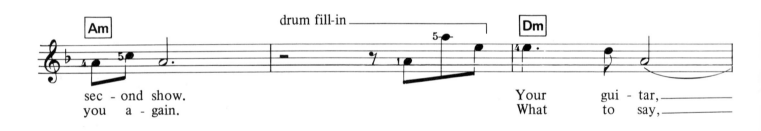

sec - ond show. Your gui - tar,
you a - gain. What to say,

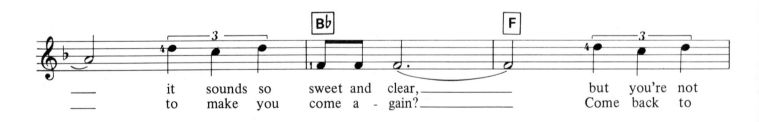

___ it sounds so sweet and clear, but you're not
___ to make you come a - gain? Come back to

real - ly here, it's just the ra - di - o.
me a - gain, and play your sad gui - tar.

Chorus

Don't you re-mem-ber you told me you love me ba - by?___ You

said you'd be com - ing back this way a - gain may - be.___

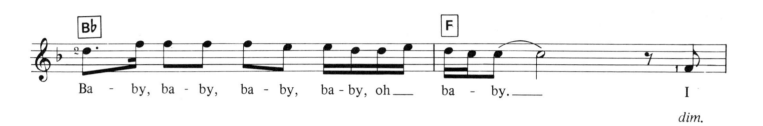

Ba - by, ba - by, ba - by, ba - by, oh___ ba - by.___ I

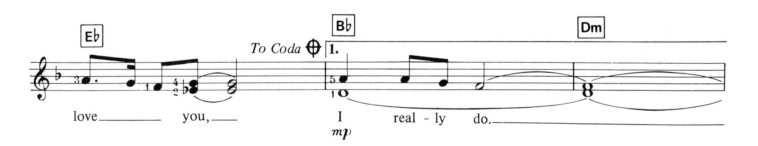

love___ you,___ I real - ly do.___

strings to clarinet

I real - ly do.___ *D.S. al Coda*

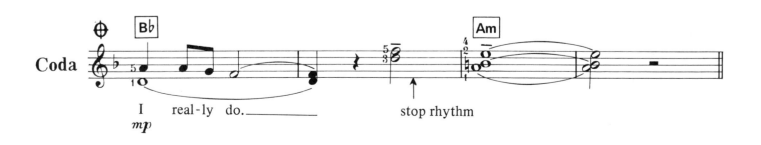

Coda

I real-ly do.___ stop rhythm

The Fool On The Hill

Words & Music by John Lennon & Paul McCartney

Voice: flute
Rhythm: rock
Tempo: medium (♩ = 92)

1. Day af - ter day, _____ a - lone on a

hill, the man with the fool - ish grin is keep - ing

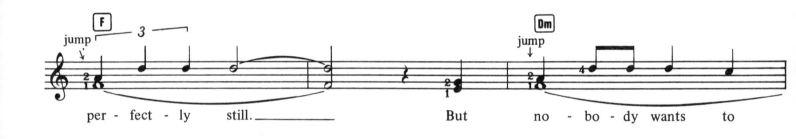

per - fect - ly still. _____ But no - bo - dy wants to

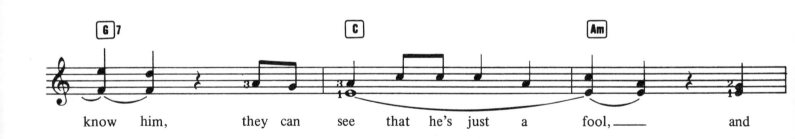

know him, they can see that he's just a fool, ____ and

he nev - er gives an an - swer, but the fool ____ on the

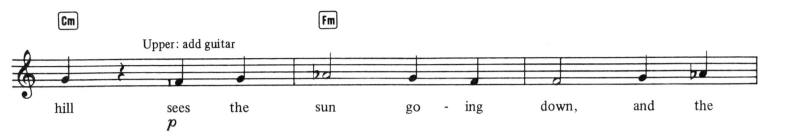

hill   sees   the   sun   go - ing   down,   and   the

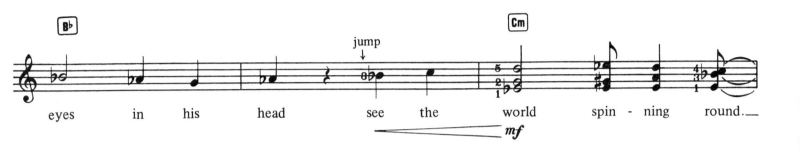

eyes   in   his   head   see   the   world   spin - ning   round.

2. Well on the way, head in a cloud,
   The man of a thousand voices talking perfectly loud.
   But nobody ever hears him, or the sound he appears to make,
   And he never seems to notice, but the fool on the hill

   Sees the sun going down, and the eyes in his head
   See the world spinning round.

3. *(Instrumental solo for 4 bars)*

   And nobody seems to like him, they can tell what he wants to do,
   And he never shows his feelings, but the fool on the hill

   See the sun going down, *(etc.)*

4. *(Instrumental solo for 4 bars)*

   He never listens to them, he knows that they're the fools
   They don't like him, the fool on the hill

   Sees the sun going down, *(etc.)*

The Name Of The Game

Words & Music by Benny Andersson, Stig Anderson & Bjorn Ulvaeus

Voice: trumpet
Rhythm: rock
Tempo: fairly fast (melody ♩ = 160)
(rhythm ♩ = 80)

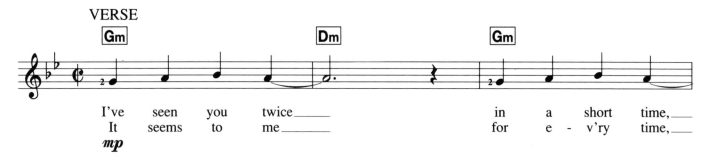

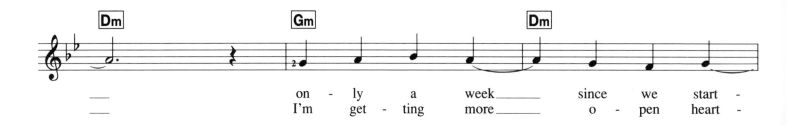

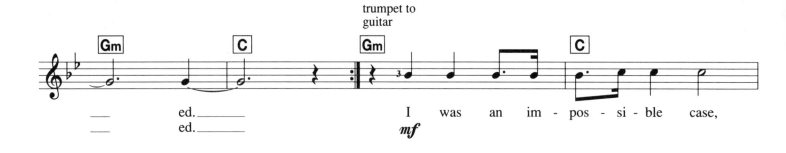

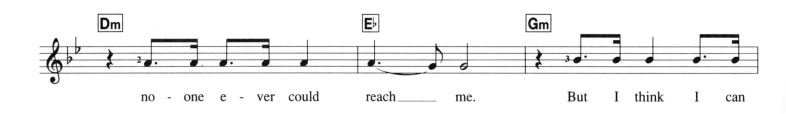

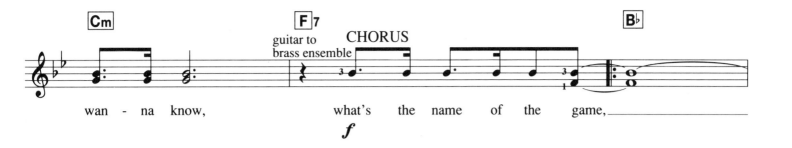

wan - na know, what's the name of the game,_____

_____ does it mean a - ny - thing_____ to you?_____

What's the name of the game,_____

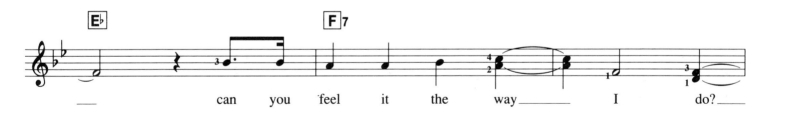

_____ can you feel it the way_____ I do?_____

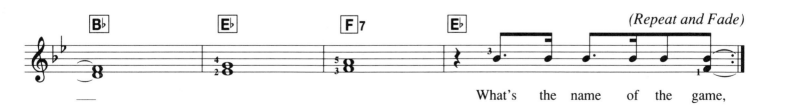

(Repeat and Fade)

_____ What's the name of the game,

The Road To Hell

WORDS & MUSIC BY CHRIS REA

Voice: flute
Rhythm: rock
Tempo: medium (♩ = 126)

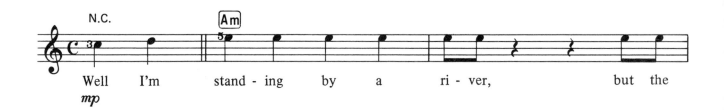

Well I'm stand - ing by a ri - ver, but the

wa - ter does - n't flow. ____ It boils with ev - 'ry poi - son ____

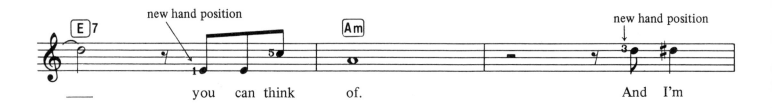

____ you can think of. And I'm

un - der - neath ____ the street lights, but the light of joy I know, ____

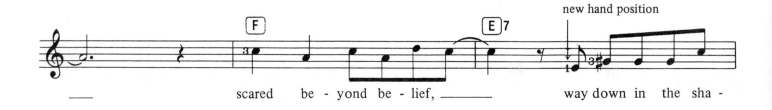

____ scared be - yond be - lief, ____ way down in the sha -

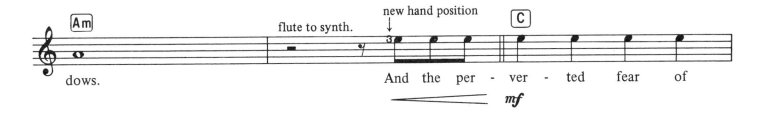

dows. And the per - ver - ted fear of

vio - lence chokes a smile on ev - 'ry face. And

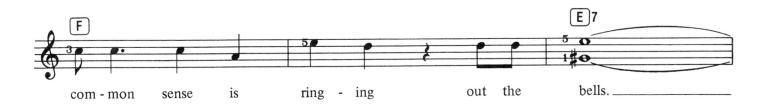

com - mon sense is ring - ing out the bells. _____

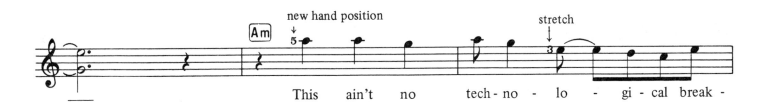

This ain't no tech - no - lo - gi - cal break -

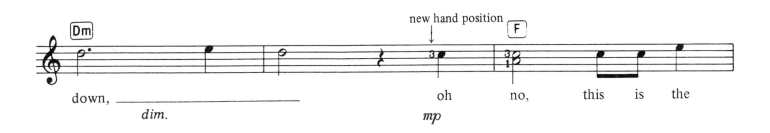

down, _____ oh no, this is the

road to hell. _____

The Sound Of Silence

Words & Music by Paul Simon

Voice: string ensemble
Rhythm: rhumba
Tempo: medium (♩ = 100)

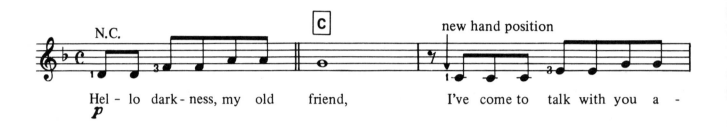

Hel - lo dark - ness, my old friend, I've come to talk with you a -

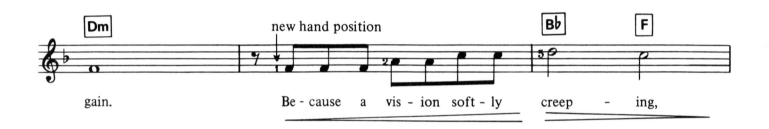

gain. Be - cause a vis - ion soft - ly creep - ing,

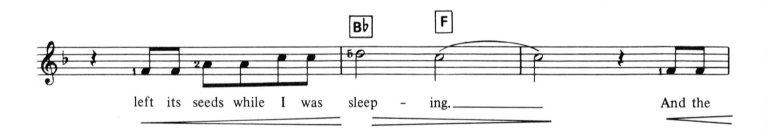

left its seeds while I was sleep - ing. And the

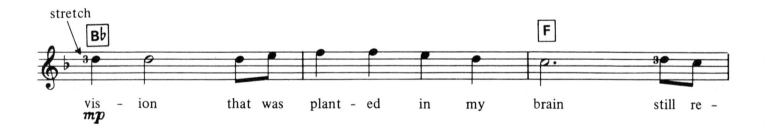

vis - ion that was plant - ed in my brain still re -

mains, with - in the sound of

si - lence.___ In rest-less dreams I walked a – lone,

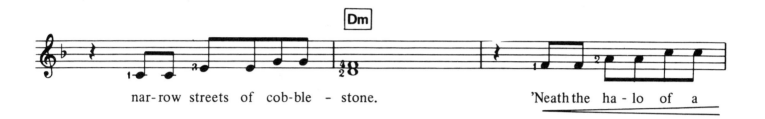

nar-row streets of cob-ble – stone. 'Neath the ha - lo of a

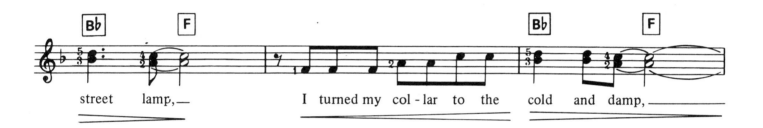

street lamp,___ I turned my col -lar to the cold and damp,___

when my eyes were stabbed by the flash of a ne – on

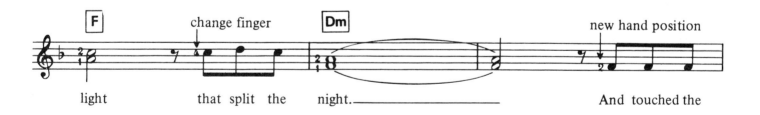

light that split the night.___ And touched the

sound of si - lence.___ stop rhythm

THE WONDER OF YOU

WORDS & MUSIC BY BAKER KNIGHT

Voice: string ensemble
Rhythm: slow rock
Tempo: slow (♩ = 68)

When no-one else can ___ un-der-stand me, ___
And when you smile, the ___ world is bright - er, ___

mp

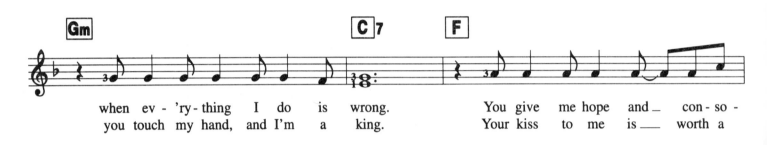

when ev-'ry-thing I do is wrong. You give me hope and ___ con-so-
you touch my hand, and I'm a king. Your kiss to me is ___ worth a

la - tion, ___ you give me hope to ___ car-ry on. And you
for - tune, ___ your love to me is ___ ev-'ry-thing. And you're

try ___ to show your love ___ for me, in ev - 'ry-thing you
al - ways there to lend ___ a hand in all ___ I try to

cresc.   *mf*

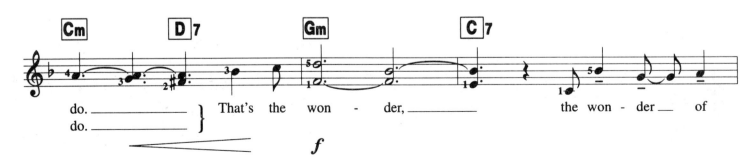

do. ___ } That's the won - der, ___ the won - der ___ of
do. ___

f

116

Till There Was You

Words & Music by Meredith Willson

Voice: guitar
Rhythm: rhumba
Tempo: medium (♩ = 100)
Synchro-start

There were bells on the hill, but I

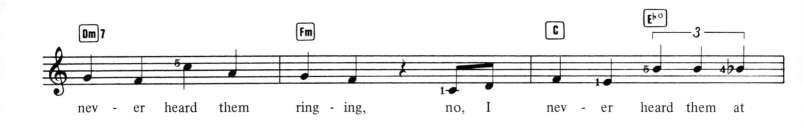

nev - er heard them ring - ing, no, I nev - er heard them at

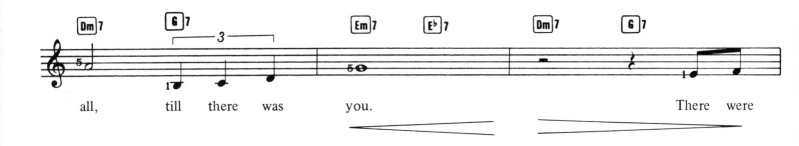

all, till there was you. There were

birds in the sky, but I nev - er saw them

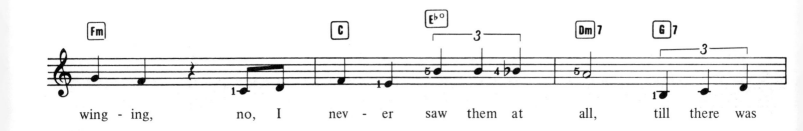

wing - ing, no, I nev - er saw them at all, till there was

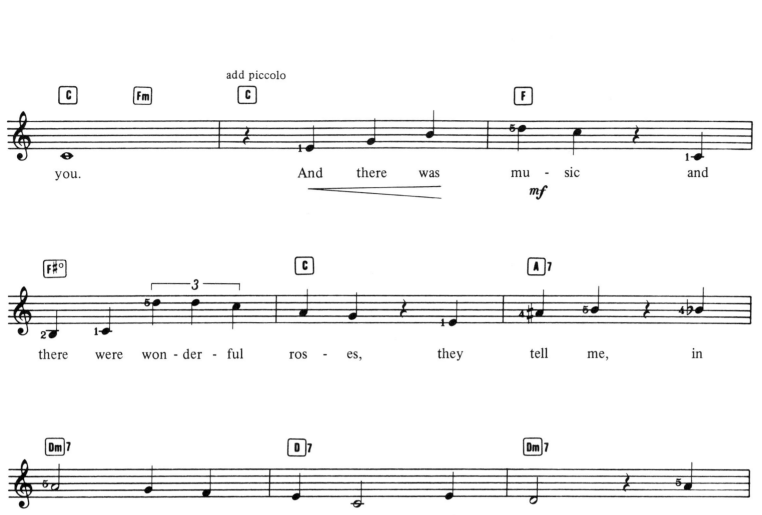

you. And there was mu - sic and

add piccolo

mf

there were won - der - ful ros - es, they tell me, in

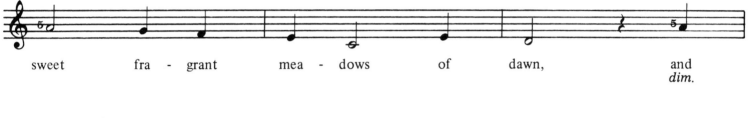

sweet fra - grant mea - dows of dawn, and

dim.

dew. There was love all a - round, but I

cut piccolo

mp

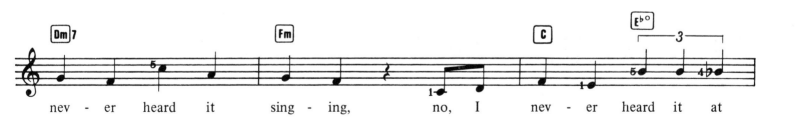

nev - er heard it sing - ing, no, I nev - er heard it at

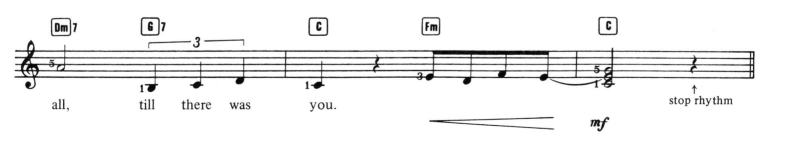

all, till there was you.

stop rhythm

mf

WHAT THE WORLD NEEDS NOW IS LOVE

WORDS BY HAL DAVID | MUSIC BY BURT BACHARACH

Voice: trumpet
Rhythm: jazz waltz
Tempo: quite fast (♩ = 132)

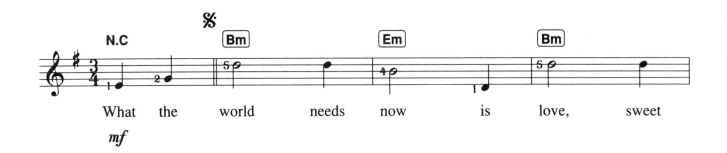

What the world needs now is love, sweet

love. It's the on - ly thing_____ that there's

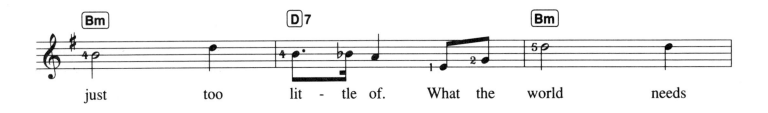

just too lit - tle of. What the world needs

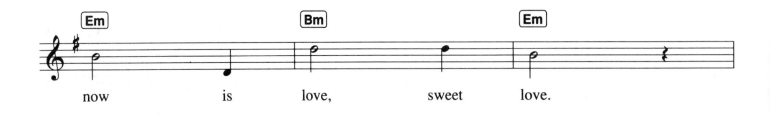

now is love, sweet love.

No, not just for some,_____ but for ev - 'ry - one._____

Lord, we don't need a-noth-er moun-tain.

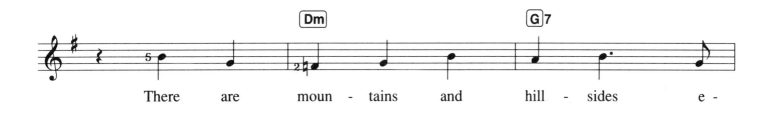

There are moun-tains and hill-sides e-

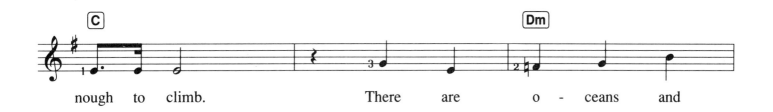

nough to climb. There are o-ceans and

riv-ers e-nough to cross,_____ e-nough to last

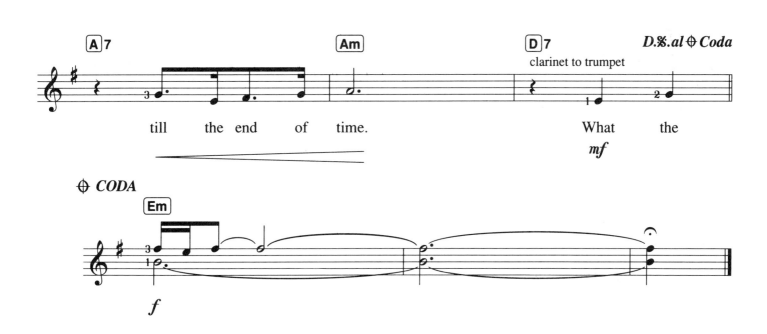

till the end of time. What the

⊕ CODA

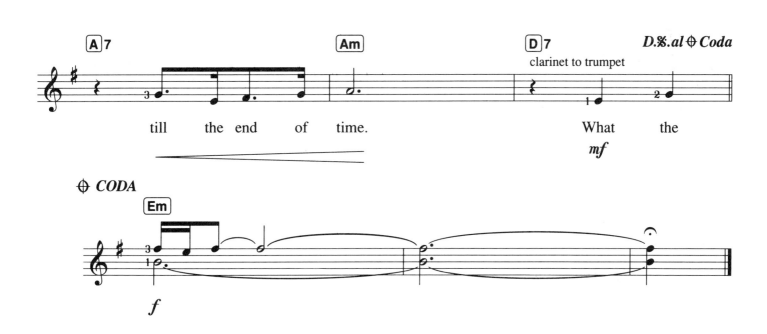

Words

Words & Music by Barry Gibb, Robin Gibb & Maurice Gibb

Voice: piano
Rhythm: rock
Tempo: fairly slow (♩ = 84)

Smile an ev-er-last-ing smile, a smile could bring you near to me.

Don't ev-er let me find you gone, 'cause that would bring a

tear to me. This world has lost its glo-ry,

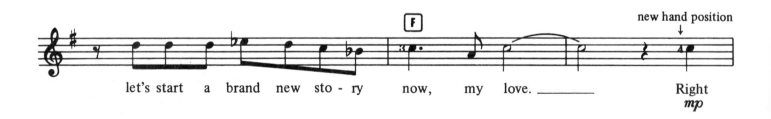

let's start a brand new sto-ry now, my love. Right

now, there'll be no oth-er time, and I can show you how, my

cross over thumb

piano to guitar

love. _____ Talk in ev - er - last-ing words, and ded - i - cate them

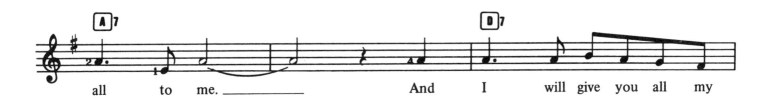

all to me. _____ And I will give you all my

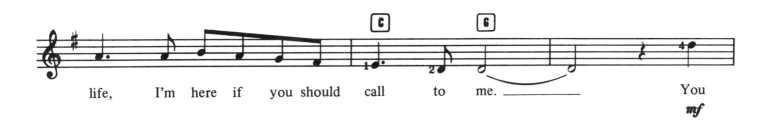

life, I'm here if you should call to me. _____ You

mf

think that I don't ev - en mean a sin - gle word I say.

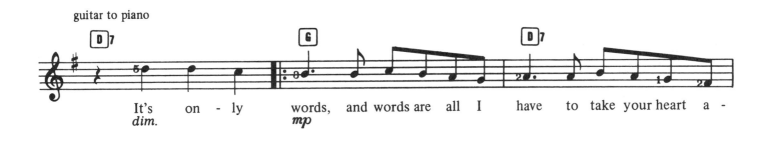

guitar to piano

It's on - ly words, and words are all I have to take your heart a -

dim.   mp

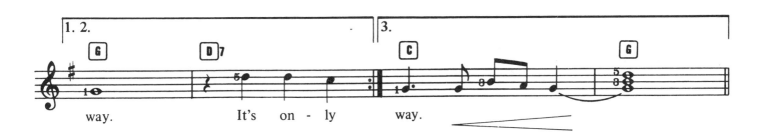

1. 2.   3.

way.   It's on - ly way.

Happy Xmas (War Is Over)

Words & Music by John Lennon & Yoko Ono

Voice: brass ensemble + saxophone
Rhythm: slow rock (or waltz)
Tempo: fast (♩ = 168)
synchro-start

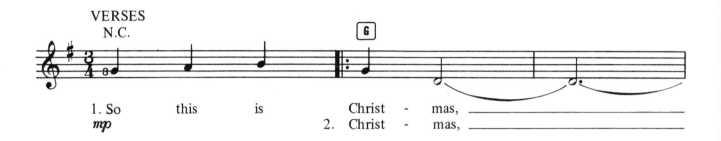

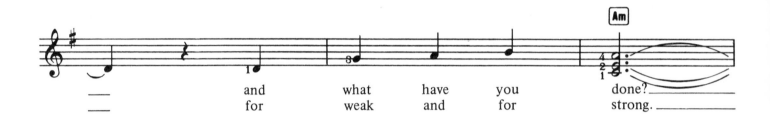

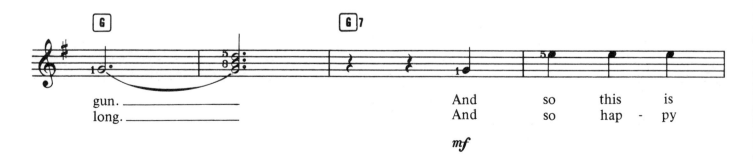

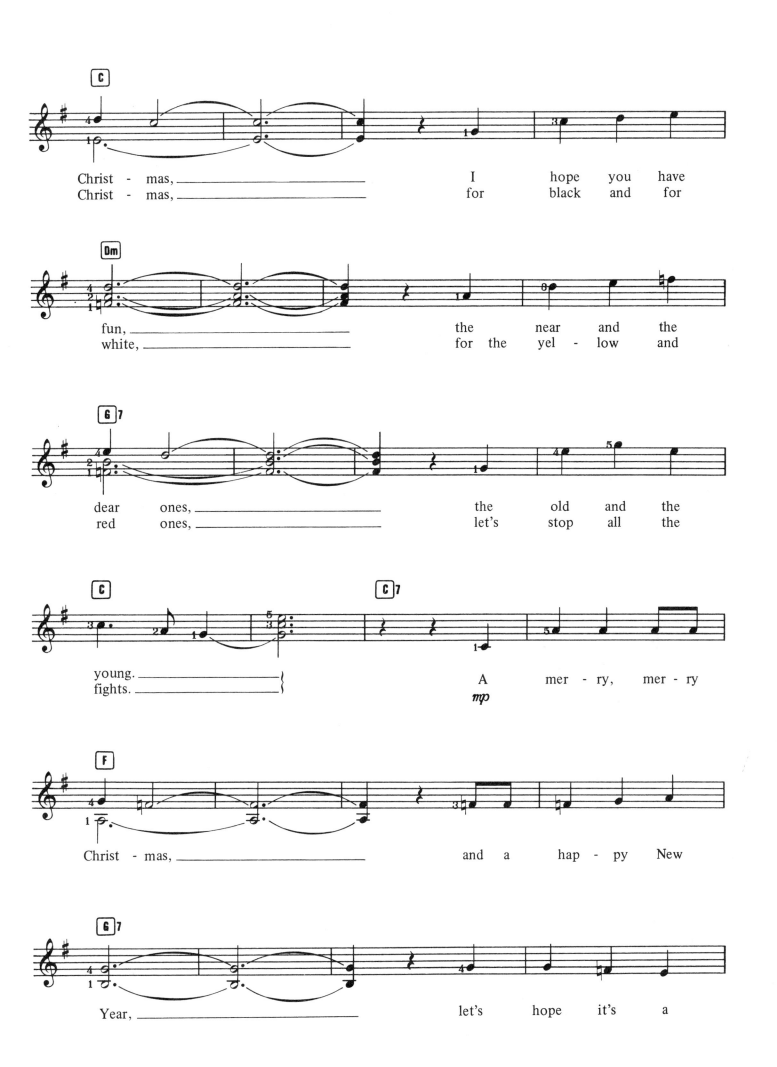

Christ - mas, _____ I hope you have
Christ - mas, _____ for black and for

fun, _____ the near and the
white, _____ for the yel - low and

dear ones, _____ the old and the
red ones, _____ let's stop all the

young. _____ A mer - ry, mer - ry
fights. _____ *mp*

Christ - mas, _____ and a hap - py New

Year, _____ let's hope it's a

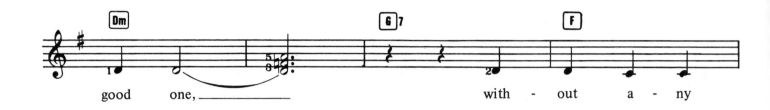

good one,_____ with - out a - ny

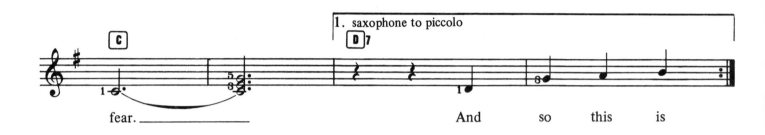

1. saxophone to piccolo

fear._____ And so this is

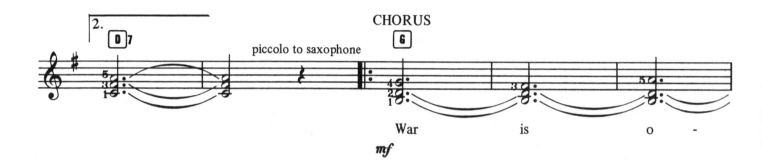

2. | CHORUS
piccolo to saxophone

mf

War is o -

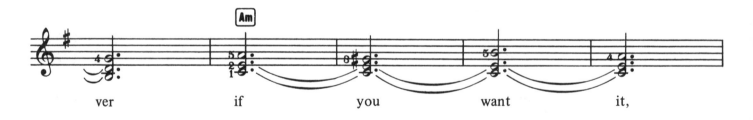

ver if you want it,

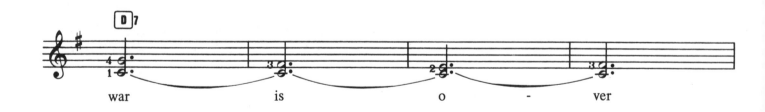

war is o - ver

(Repeat and Fade)

now._____